MIURA!

Acclaim for Nicholas Anderson

Writing under a pseudonym, a former spy irreverently dissects his work for Britain's Secret Intelligence Service (MI6), where he worked between 1973 and 1993, in this "documentary thriller." Scoffing at the glamorous James Bond image, the author summarizes the world of intelligence as a dismal struggle among predators. Despite his conscious straddling of the border between faction and fiction, Anderson presents scenes vividly, including his break-in to a Libyan chemical weapons plant and his encounters with famed terrorist Carlos the Jackal. The author moves from the intricacies of espionage to the money-hungry machinations of pharmaceutical companies. His theme here is not espionage as such, but rather his life as a spy. And, the experiences he describes in the first person infuse his work with an informed, if disenchanted, perspective that will appeal to anyone interested in the world of intelligence operations.

Publishers Weekly, USA

Had Ian Fleming's James Bond been a real person born after the end of the cold war, into a new world order, and imbued with an existentialist bent, he'd have been Nicholas Anderson, the figure at the heart of *NOC: Non-Official Cover*. It covers over 20 years in a life spent behind the scenes of some of the most covert actions by world governments; the vast majority of whose citizens would never believe happened – or wish to.

NOC is a travelogue into both palaces of the rich and the seediest, impoverished hellholes imaginable, as the author recounts his stints as a mole for most notably, Great Britain.

Written stirringly in the first person, Anderson treats the reader with a stream-of-consciousness internal dialogue to the actions and events as they unfold around him, and peppers his tale with flashbacks of an exotic childhood, intriguing characters who float around him as either nemesis or bit player, and a global perspective that's always bracing, searingly honest and often witty.

Along the way there's enough sex, real danger and drama to make this one of the most pleasurable reads in years.

Barnes & Noble USA, customer review

NOC 4:
Addendum

by Nicholas Anderson

Print version: ISBN 978-1-7329661-6-1
eBook version: ISBN 978-1-7329661-7-8

Library of Congress Cataloguing in Publication

DEFENCE AND SECURITY MEDIA ADVISORY – NOTICE SYSTEM

In 2015 the United Kingdom's Defence and Security Media Advisory – Notice System (DSMA-NS) replaced the DA-Notice system (changed from the D-Notice in 1993 to reflect its voluntary/advisory nature), which was overseen by the Defence, Press and Broadcasting Advisory Committee (DPBAC). DPBAC was originally formed in 1912 to prevent Britain's World War I enemy, Germany, from collecting usable information from British newspapers. During World War II, the D-Notice was temporarily replaced by the more rigidly enforced Defence of the Realm Regulations and reinstated after hostilities had ended. The objective of the newly introduced DSMA-NS is to prevent inadvertent public disclosure of information that would compromise UK military and intelligence operations and methods. I hereby attest that I have not knowingly compromised UK military and intelligence operations and methods. But I remain interested in interrupting the silent course of secret proceedings (read as official lies) by UK government organs against the liberty of British citizens, and others. Even the rules about the rules are classified. D-, DA- or DMSA-NS, in capital letters or lower case, are notices that are designed by the self-appointed custodians to control veracity.

– ██████████████, Cmdr., CMG; Royal Navy, SIS, NATO, NOC, COPENHAGEN, BERNE, MOSCOW, TIRANA, BEIRUT (1951-).

* * * * * * * * * *

It remains the (British) government's policy
not to comment on contacts which an individual may
or may not have had with the security and intelligence services.

– John Major, British Prime Minister, 1990-1997

Chiefs, known as C's, at the Secret Intelligence Service (SIS is also known as MI6) that 'Nicholas Anderson' served under (7):

1973-1983:
John Rennie, 1968-1973
Maurice Oldfield, 1973-1978
Arthur 'Dickie' Franks, 1978-1982
Colin Figures, 1982-1985

1992-1993:
Colin McColl, 1989-1994

2003-2007:
Richard Dearlove, 1999-2004
John Scarlett, 2004-2009

Note: Contradictorily, no deputy head of SIS has ever been publicly named.

* * * * * * * * * *

While MI5 and GCHQ have declassified a small and carefully selected number of files, in a manner that no doubts sculpts a favourable history, MI6 has not made public a single page of any of the files that it has created since its foundation in 1909.
MI6 insists that this secrecy is required to safeguard the identities of its sources. The risks of retribution, according to the agency, can extend beyond a single generation. MI6 also maintains that many of its records consist principally of information relating to agents and sources, and that there is no body of records containing assessments of intelligence or foreign policy.

— Ian Cobain, author, *The History Thieves*

* * * * * * * * * *

*A person who is truly free
does not belong to any religion,
political party or belief system.*

Foreword

During times of universal deceit, telling the truth becomes a revolutionary act.
(This quote, though of uncertain origin, is mistakenly attributed to George Orwell.)

As a result of much positive feedback received after the publication of *The NOC Trilogy*, I have concluded that a fourth book of mine would go a long way towards satisfying the interest of the public. This latest instalment deals with topics about my life that were not covered in the first three books. From my side of the fence, I did not include all of my life's stories in the earlier books due to space and page count constraints. In a sense, this is my chance to get these accounts out of my head and in front of readers' eyes. They are presented in chronological order. Each narrative relates to a stand-alone event in time and is not in any way inter-connected to other events. They are the anecdotes of this former Secret Intelligence Service (SIS/MI6) intelligence officer who has lived through them. I joined SIS in 1973 and served for almost 20 years in three stints – finally retiring in 2007. Subsequently volunteering for one tasking order in 2008.

Being an avid fan of George Orwell, I have read most of his books. Since his death, I'm not aware of anyone else, apart from Noam Chomsky, who has taken up his mantle and addressed the issue of how the future will take shape. So, this is my opportunity to offer my predictions on the way ahead, as I see the future unfolding. There is a word which both those authors frequently used that applied often to my occupational hazard: 'doublethink' – the ability to have two contradictory ideas in mind and believe both of them (on page 27 of Orwell's *Nineteen-Eighty-Four* published in 1983). Doublethink situations existed in covert action operations at SIS.

In this respect, material in this book covers incidences in my life and career viewed in hindsight, with foresight added at times to the mix. In spy jargon this is described as 'walking the cat back' (attempting to understand circumstances by reconstructing events chronologically from the present to the past).

Looking back at the early days of my career, I can now see why there was an old saying that SIS 'wanted to enlist those people who had already lived their life'. In my own case, I have finally reached my inner peace. I am able and eager to tell you about my calling. Failing to do so would have shackled my soul.

* * * * * * * * *

Soon after passing my driver's test as a teenager – perhaps I was 17 – in the northeast of England, I suffered the kind of embarrassment that most youngsters of my age experienced…asking my father if I could borrow his car on the weekend to go to clubs with my pals. He kindly assented to my pleadings most of the time.

His white Hillman Minx's licence plate at the time, amazingly, was SPY73. By sheer happenstance, I started training to be an SIS intelligence officer in 1973 – but back then, the prospect never entered my head. Passing my exams at college, playing football and getting to know some girls was where my head was at the time – like most lads my age.

But looking back as a retired old war-horse with a greying mane, writing this quasi-memoir, it is quite remarkable to think that my father owned such a unique and prophetic custom-made plate. While growing up, his own real career was unknown to me. Only later, when I began mine, did I find out that he was a spy himself. I can only surmise that in some strange way, my future was almost pre-ordained. I would eventually become a deep cover intelligence officer after my Royal Navy Fleet Air Arm service was cut short due to a career-changing injury in Laos. *I was seconded to the Secret Intelligence Service, also known as MI6, in 1973.* My training in tradecraft took place over six months in London's Palace Street, close to Buckingham Palace, Fort Monckton in Gosport on the English Channel (actually a Napoleonic fortification next to a golf course), and other locations I am still not at liberty to mention. I graduated from the IONEC (intelligence officers new entry course) in 1974 and was sent on my first reconnoitre that very same year.

Was it really possible for my father to choreograph the course of my life and predict it five full years before it actually unfolded? And on top of that to continue my education by attending a university in Moscow for a year, at 19, to learn Russian. I can never fully answer this perplexing enigma, I'm afraid. It is simply too hard to believe that my late father had groomed me to do this kind of work for Queen and country. I was later also seconded to the North Atlantic Treaty Organisation (NATO). Looking back, and with the benefit of hindsight, I can now see how my father and his cronies protected me by pushing some buttons and pulling strings even after I was accepted into Her Majesty's armed forces and security apparatuses and at other key points throughout my career.

When I entered SIS proper, the service was just emerging from some of its darkest days. Their operations had been severely compromised following the betrayal by the so-called Cambridge Five (five senior SIS intelligence officers had spied for the Soviet Union for decades before defecting). Many of the agents in SIS foreign networks were uncovered and most lost their lives. As a result of these and other colossal failures, SIS massively revamped itself from top to bottom and was starting a new page. To protect me and unbeknownst to me at the time, my dad made sure that I would not be left uncovered in the event of another security breach. A *cordon sanitiere*, a measure designed to prevent penetration by outside influences, was implemented by the Joint Action Committee. (JAC operated from 1964 to 1991.) Once I was assigned to the Directorate of Production/SOV, specialising in all matters to do with the USSR and its satellites behind the Iron Curtain, only two other people knew my real name. My true identity was kept under lock in the two separate safes located respectively at the Foreign & Commonwealth Office (FCO) and the Ministry of Defence (MoD). SIS were never made aware of my real name. I was one of the few new recruits at the recently reformed SIS to have their own BIGOT list. BIGOT is a 'bacronym' of TO GIB, an old codename from WWII when allied forces were sent to Gibraltar. The list identifies those people cleared to know about any military or intel operation I was involved in. Thus, I was given an assumed name, with a full cover ID. My fellow officers that I worked with at SIS only knew me by this cover name and the same applied to my neighbours where I lived.

Simultaneously, during this reorganisation at SIS that came into being around 1970, a decision was made to work closer with the Central Intelligence Agency (CIA), the counterpart agency of the US. *It was the beginning of Britain becoming a terrorist state for the United States in that we did their dirty work for them.* As a result of this new cooperation, and not long after commencing operational duties with SIS, I was selected to participate in a non-official cover (NOC) role for NATO. The operation was European-based but it was run by the Americans using their own preferred codes and slang. (Natural cover is the term for undercover by SIS.) NOCs were mostly CIA but with a handful of SIS officers working outside the umbrella of an embassy or consulate who were usually assigned denied (black) operations. As such, they did not enjoy diplomatic protection if captured. So, I became one of the first British SIS intelligence officers assigned under NATO's NOC clandestine operations – *the most secret of the secret* – …useful in the front line because he or she is not readily identified as acting on behalf of any particular government. Additionally, the actions of NOC officers often involved paramilitary operations that were either classified (filed under secret and top secret) or unclassified (verbalised only). The latter could never be declassified as no classified file was ever created.

Interestingly, too, there were three types of covert action: defensive, preventative and offensive.

As NOCs were a new entity to those who knew of their existence at SIS, some bright spark in London came up with this four-point panoptic view of our work:

1. Not everything is quite as it seems
2. Observe, digest, assess the source, who has to be credible then verifiable
3. Conclude, it is what it is
4. Share your findings

Lastly, though both my parents were British, I was born in the colonies. I mixed early with people from all backgrounds and cultures. To a large extent and because of my upbringing, I grew up as a child of the empire. As an adult, I now consider myself a citizen of the planet. Through my eyes I will always see myself as such: an international person determined to advance the unfulfilled promise of a better future for mankind. I do not exclusively focus on any particular point of view be it left, centre or right political angle. Nor do I limit myself to Britain-only issues. In my intelligence career, I was mostly tasked with observing and reporting back, but then had to think next how to solve the problem for the betterment of all. I'm still doing that in 'overcover' (retirement).

In a sentence: I'm someone who lives in the moment. I think that sums up who I was and still am to this day. I don't think I will ever be able to ride off into the sunset. There's still too much of this imperfect wonderful world to experience.

* * * * * * * *

One job of fiction is to travel to the places where reporting fails because the participants can't or won't talk.

— Mark Lawson, *Guardian*

I realise that nobody in the West cares anymore about the outcome of a gruesome incident that took place over a decade ago. The events leading to it, occurred in 2004 in North Ossetia, a remote part of Russia practically no one had heard of before. But the European Court of Human Rights eventually issued a scathing ruling on the horrific massacre in Beslan that claimed the lives of more than 330 hostages. The final report published in April 2017, places direct blame on the Russian security forces. In that respect it wholly supports my own on-the-scene and eyewitness account of the bloody incident as I describe it in book 3 of my trilogy published in 2016 (in pages 192 to 211, if you care to read it again).

Ironically, I am assembling and including in this fourth book, the bits 'n' pieces that I had to omit way back then for a number of reasons. In the first place, some of the information was still restricted at the time and I did not want to run afoul of my previous employer. But over time some details have become open source material. Secondly, I had to contend with space limitations. With the benefit of hindsight, I will also be addressing events where changes and/or newly available knowledge shed a different light on those past events.

It should be known that in situations where NOC deep cover tasks are undertaken, those participating in a specific operation are verbally informed as follows: *"This next is sensitive source information – no further dissemination of action is to be taken without reference to XXX."* Those that received this rather ambiguously-worded message in person instantly understood that the mission they were about to embark on, would either be denied or the eventual outcome would be covered up. I will not ever disclose what the 3X's stood for. I will only say it is a secret unit based in the Foreign and Commonwealth Office's London headquarters.

Usually, if any records were kept, it is noticeable there are significant gaps.

I am mentioning this to you now as this kind of similar government doublespeak wording and its ultimate conclusion will be amply featured in this fourth book. Somebody has to disclose the shenanigans that go on and the multiple layers of protection. I am perfectly happy to be that person. We live in a world filled with hypocrisies that need to be exposed.

* * * * * * * * *

In my third book *NOC Three Times: Knock-On Effect (Last of the Trilogy)*, I have recounted the many stories of the 30 British élite special forces that I had the privilege to serve with in Iraq, Iran, Somalia, Yemen and Afghanistan. They were handpicked from the Special Air Service and the Special Boat Service. But the exploits of these modern-day 'uncammo' (not in uniform) warriors did not end with my retirement from being their first commander in the field. Due to the unheralded achievements of our unit, it was reorganised in April 2005 and became officially called Special Reconnaissance Detachment (SpR). Since then, SpR has evolved into a Special Reconnaissance Regiment that now numbers as many as 40 highly-trained soldiers. Its focus remains, as it was back then, on carrying out 'very specific tasks'. As it was then, and to this day, whatever the true masters of the dark arts secretly achieve, will never be announced. What I disclosed is probably the most ever revealed without divulging any confidential information. It will be denied anyway.

From a personal point of view, looking back on those days, I take great satisfaction from establishing a strict *averse-Rashomon effect* among those lads. The Rashomon effect is used in intelligence to explain a situation when there are contradictory interpretations by the many individuals involved. It was so named after Japanese director Akira Kurosawa's 1950 film of the same name where witnesses described differing outcomes to the same incident. I managed to get all my diverse group of personalities on the same page operating towards clearly defined goals with getaway game plans executed successfully.

Note: When I retired in 2007, an élite team, known as E squadron was established as a composite force of SAS, SBS and SpR personnel. Confusing media reports have made out E squadron and SpR are both one and the same. It is incorrect even though some members of SpR are seconded to E squadron.

＊ ＊ ＊ ＊ ＊ ＊ ＊ ＊ ＊

Two US Navy SEALs have published books on widely distributed major imprints to much marketing fanfare. The two versions of events from the pair who were first into the room and claiming to kill Osama bin Laden (OBL) in Abbottabad, Pakistan, on 2 May 2011 are completely contradictory. The first publication lacks the 'stamp of approval' and endorsement of the US government. The second book, issued several years later, appears to have won the approval of the master class at the Pentagon and the White House. They were clearly determined to steal the limelight and take unwarranted credit for the death of OBL. *But I know differently.*

In the third book of my trilogy, I told the world at length of the UK's unpublicised account of the death of OBL. It is based on a meticulously-planned operation that took place on 11 October 2005, in the Hindu Kush, Afghanistan, some *five and half years prior* to the purported demise of OBL. The site of the skirmish is only 40 miles away as the crow flies from where the Americans later made their claim to fame and glory. To further inject a sense of credibility to their claims, the Americans unabashedly supported the production of a big budget Hollywood movie. The blockbuster guns-blazing type of action movie eventually won an Oscar after attaining several nominations. *Ironically, no one stopped to ask why no dead body has ever been presented as evidence.*

Well, let me tell you what the bottom line is in this brief sitrep (situation report): The CIA's headquarters in Langley, Virginia, from an early time housed a highly classified section codenamed 'Elvis', their internal codename for OBL. Its specific remit was to concentrate on tracking down the Al-Qaida leader and once located, to eliminate him forthwith. Significantly enough, on 3 July 2006, the non-profit Washington, DC-based National Public Radio, and a syndicator to 900 radio stations across America, reported that the "CIA unit responsible for finding Osama bin Laden was shuttered in late-2005."

There was a valid reason for the low-key closure of that office, if you care to pay attention to what happened in Afghanistan during that *exact same timeframe.* Needless to state few if any in the American mainstream media picked up on this important but purposely well-hidden clue. Instead, it evidently chose years later to parrot and disseminate the press releases of their government's propaganda machine. The so-called free press willingly or gullibly participated in a steady drum-beat to force a charade on the unsuspecting nation.

If you still can't connect the dots, then I will spell it out for you, the reader. *The CIA no longer maintained an office on OBL because he no longer existed. The information of OBL's likely demise was conveyed to them only a month or two earlier by their British counterparts. As it was, the British had a live satellite feed of the massive explosion that must have killed him. Certainly, he was never heard from again from that moment onwards. Furthermore, the clothes found in the supposedly dead man's closet by two SIS officers based in nearby Islamabad shortly after the incident, confirmed they were too small to fit his lanky frame.*

Perhaps the reason for this continued silence is the British were always reinforcing our key strategic relationship with the US...where we wore the collar while they were holding the leash!

* * * * * * * * *

I am gratified to note that since publication of *The NOC Trilogy* one aspect espoused throughout the three books is finally recognised and embraced by a small but growing minority among the intellectual class.

The all-encompassing word I use to define this emerging movement is *dégage* (French for clear-out). It's a new philosophy adopted by the people of the world that have had enough of the old ways of doing things and the patronising elitism of the ruling class. There is a determination to rebel against the existing political system by not electing the conventional party candidates and opting instead for change – *for better or for worse*. I am one of those keen on shaking up our society. We the people cannot keep on doing the same old, even going backwards in time. Let's move forward on to new unexplored pastures. *I firmly believe that the current system of voting for one party is obsolete and long dead*. The days of politicians participating in brinkmanship must be relegated to the dustbin of history. With modern technology, a secure encrypted application can be developed to allow the public to individually vote on each specific policy or issue they support. The politicians' role, regardless of the party they represent, would then be to carry out the wishes of the people. Failure to do so means they would be voted out and replaced by more responsive elected officials. Emphasis would switch from the party as a whole being in power to the individual policies they create. This should be the new communal standard for governance in the 21st century and beyond.

* * * * * * * * *

If they can get you asking the wrong questions,
they don't have to worry about the answers.
    – Thomas Pynchon, American novelist

The above quote is self-evident to me on how the political discourse has deteriorated in our present-day society. Sadly, it accurately reflects the stale state of affairs even in many of today's so-called democratic nations. It is borne out from our western society's abject surrender to political correctness (PC). Bottom-line questions are not asked for fear of upsetting those that cleverly created this situation of not delving too deeply. But to me it's a slogan of sorts that sweeps inconvenient truths and 'taboo' issues under the carpet. *Issues must be fully addressed in the open*. Rebel against the fashionable interpretation of PC and ask more meaningful questions! By failing to do so, you are docilely relinquishing your power to force change. In such case you deserve to be manipulated like sheep ready for shearing.

* * * * * * * * * *

In the intervening literary lulls between writing my books I have had the opportunity to travel back to some of the places where significant and memorable adventures had taken place decades earlier.

Of the countries I re-visited, the most memorable trips were to the Czech Republic (formerly Czechoslovakia and now wishing to be known as Czechia), Cuba, Bulgaria and Laos.

In Prague I took for the second time in my life a boat ride down the picturesque Vltava River, which means wild water. And lo and behold, I spotted the very same vessel that the then chieftain of the Irish Republican Army and I had met on in the early nineties. He had flown from New York City and I drove from Moscow for a fateful meeting. On this recent trip, the floating barge was moored in close proximity to one of the city's 18 magnificent bridges. The riverboat, named Czechie, is still painted in the same colour shamrock green as she was way back then.

In Cuba, I travelled for three weeks around the country and visited most of the same places I had seen during an earlier trip in 1993. I have now been to Cuba four times, the first in 1969 with this last trip in 2016. Each visit presented me with a different experience and perspective. At the Che Guevara museum housed inside the imposing fortress across the river mouth from Old Havana, I was the sole visitor present at the time. During my visit, my walking stick suddenly gave up the ghost; the handle broke off ironically right in front of a photo of Che holding his own cane in his hands. Minutes later, I tumbled out into the sunshine. Across the street was a hole in the wall selling hand-made timbered goods, with no other shop in sight. There was on display only one wooden staff – a solidly stout one. So I bought it, and ever since it has been my inseparable companion. It has become a prized possession. To my mind, its ownership by me was meant to be.

In Bulgaria I took a slow train ride from a stop near Sofia airport to Plovdiv, in the south, where my daughter was scheduled to perform the next day. A talented professionally-trained ballerina, she was on an Eastern

European tour with her American-based dance company.

In preparation for this trip, I did some research on prisons in Bulgaria. I had been incarcerated for 11 weeks on spying charges in the mid-seventies. Understandably, I was keen to confirm the exact location of my holding pen. The main information publicly available on jails in Bulgaria was furnished to me through a non-governmental organisation based in Helsinki, of all places. I had always known I'd been imprisoned in a location without windows. All along I assumed I had been held in either Lovech or Skravena – Bulgaria's two main jails where foreigners suspected of a crime against the state were usually sent. It turns out my assumptions were disproven by a key clue: upon release from my prison cell, I remembered the uncomfortable journey rolling in the back of a fast-moving van. Even though I had been drugged, the trip could not have lasted more than a couple of hours to the Bulgarian-Turkish border crossing. I fortunately noticed that the checkpoint was named Kapitan Andreevo. Lovech is located 150 km north of Sofia, while Skravena lies 41 km northeast of the Bulgarian capital. It would have been impossible to cover the respective distance from either prison in such a short a time.

The Finland-based non-profit then suggested I may have been held instead in one of four detention centres. The only underground facility where detainees were kept in solitary confinement in a cell measuring 4' x 6' (1.3 m x 1.8m), was reportedly located in a municipality called Pazardzhik, some 37 km west of Plovdiv. Since Plovdiv was on my itinerary, and despite well-founded reservations, I endeavoured to make a slight detour towards Pazardzhik and pay a visit to the infamous jail. However, I didn't know that the slow train en route to Plovdiv would actually make a scheduled stop in Pazardzhik. When the name suddenly appeared above the railway station's platform my world turned upside down. I momentarily returned to the dark reality of the distant past. The whole experience took probably less than a minute. But the chill from the memory of the torture I suffered there ran across all the pain points of my body like pinpricks and then dissipated. The sight of the town from the tracks as the train chugged out of it was nondescript and grey, still looking very communist era. Yes, it was emotionally creepy.

I never returned to Pazardzhik as I had originally planned. Soon after arrival in Plovdiv, I went into the main tourist office. The well-intentioned

Bulgarian girl, who was the lone information attendant at that time, surprisingly pulled up images of the detention centre on her computer screen. Yes, that same tingle ran down my back again while viewing the photos. I probably would like to forget its address, which she volunteered to me without even being prompted. It was, she said, "153 Georgi Benkovski Boulevard, Pazardzhik." It's a place where I suffered and survived the worst imaginable horror of my life…

Her voice continued to echo in my head as she was reciting the directions to the prison, "You go A1 road northwest, left at exit 37, junction of 8 and 37, and it is in front of you." Then she stopped talking and turned her attention to serve another tourist. All I could see at that moment in front of me, was a void of absolutely nothing at all for a minute. All the while, I heard the voice of someone invisible to me screaming at me in Russian. I suddenly snapped to and found myself outside that office walking away in a daze. Notwithstanding my harsh treatment years ago, I'm pleased to confirm that Plovdiv today is one of the nicest places I have ever encountered in my world travels.

And just in case you wondered, my daughter danced brilliantly in the local theatre the next day, too. It made the trip well worth it!

A note, on being tortured: The experience lives inside you like a dark vault in a pitch-black endless cave with no light – that you can't find the way out of. I'm quite proud of myself for having overcome a stage of extreme negativity. I was able to move forward in the belief that the elusive ray of hope would eventually be found. I am glad to report that I indeed found it.

Lastly, but not least, I also recently visited Laos – a dirt poor landlocked nation. I'd been shot down in my Royal Navy helicopter in the early-seventies while the Vietnam War was still raging next door. The trip was inspiring to me when I arrived back there 44 years later. The British government's secret Joint Action Committee (JAC) that was responsible for deniable covert action operations in south-east Asia had long closed down in the mid-seventies. In the old-world capital of Vientiane, I went to the NGO, COPE (Cooperative Orthotic & Prosthetic Enterprise) that still to this day deals with the innocent victims of America's blanket and wanton bombing of Laos. The UXO (unexploded ordnance) remains on the ground at a shockingly high level. As an aside and appeal, please find time to learn about COPE and their extraordinary work on behalf of all those who lost limbs. And if you can, consider donating to their cause.

Next, making my way to the north, the nearest I could get to the former Golden Triangle (until the early 21st century most of the world's heroin came from this region that covers Myanmar [Burma], Thailand and Laos), was a wonderful riverside town called Luang Prabang. It looked the same though, like nothing had changed in over four decades. So, I immersed myself into its peaceful Buddhist environment. A strange thing happened there though, my watch suddenly stopped and it didn't start again until I left Laos. I found that rather karmic.

More people should start paying attention to what's going on around them rather than being fixated on the technology in their hands. It will promote their metacognition (awareness and understanding of one's own thought processes) and their minds' well-being (mental health). Both processes ultimately open up the person to much wider possibilities.

* * * * * * * * *

What I read in the Western press and what I witnessed all over the world somehow did not match. Failed feudal states were hailed as "vibrant democracies", oppressive religious regimes were described as "tolerant" and "moderate" countries, while nationalist and socialist-oriented states were incessantly demonised, their indigenous and alternative development and social models vilified and portrayed in the bleakest colours imaginable.

Brilliant propagandists in London and Washington made sure to "protect" the public all over the world from "uncomfortable truths". Public opinion, ideology and perceptions were manufactured. And like mass-produced cars or smartphones, they were marketed through advertisement and propaganda.

I did not write those two paragraphs but a Czech-American named Andre Vltchek did in a preface for a book he had co-written with Noam Chomsky. I faithfully reproduced his words because this is exactly what I witnessed in my own travels abroad for the SIS. And because I knew this random blindness and selective amnesia went on, I spent enormous time and energy looking *beyond* what was initially presented to me in the forefront. I tried to discover forces that were manipulating the image and subtext being sent to 'unbrain' us. I define the term 'unbrain' as depriving people of the right to know the reality; to spread institutionalised disinformation for their own disproportionate gain, for power. It could also be decoded as 'dumbing the people down by design'.

Because I've been inside The Doughnut, the circular offices of Government Communications Headquarters – visitors must wear red badges; blocks A and B are the most secretive – I remain mindful what GCHQ (Britain's equivalent of the US' National Security Agency) HSOC (human science operations cell) has in store for stage-managing the British people with their carefully implemented S4 (science, signals intelligence, skills, systems) – which is another kind of perception management.

I have attempted to describe what really went on behind the scenes to manipulate the people and deliberately drive them to think in a certain direction. Because I was there, I have tried to tell it from *the inside out, not from the outside in.*

* * * * * * * * *

Prologue

My induction and schooling to become an SIS intelligence officer began in 1973 and ran into 1974. In total, the intensive course extended over a period of six long months. This new phase of my life commenced right after my military career came to a premature end. I had sustained a career-ending injury during a covert combat operation in Laos while serving as a helicopter pilot in the Royal Navy (internally known in the British government as a dark-blue aviator.)

In view of my unique educational background, language skills and armed forces experience, I had been recommended and accepted to this training programme, which included a robust mix of classroom preparation and gruelling field exercise. My time was mostly split between London and Fort Monckton, a historic military fort overlooking the English Channel in Hampshire. Built originally to protect Portsmouth harbour, the site now serves as the field operations training centre for the SIS.

Prior to being dispatched to one of the many unquiet frontiers of the world, we spent considerable time in a classroom setting learning a wide array of subjects. The syllabus included courses in behavioural science (both reading and projecting body language), psychology, as well as military history. Other topics covered acronyms, cartography, coordinates, Morse code (it's not dots and dashes but dits and das), lip reading and unique action messages (secret hand signals). Our trainers taught us helpful ways to memorise and retain details of field observations. Additionally, we learned to develop a "cover identity" that was often based on actual biographical details of our own selves.

As part of our field training, we acquired the important skills needed to effectively function as a SIS intelligence officer. The outdoor disciplines included tradecraft (techniques, methods and specialised tools used in espionage), unarmed combat and use of various weapons and firearms. Just as an example, when shooting with a pistol, we were told to double tap (fire twice) into the easier-to-hit central mass area of the target's body. Capping the fieldcraft teaching curriculum were exhausting survival courses for day and night work. During all stages of our grounding, we were under constant expert observation. The training officers were on the lookout *for individuals who could make rational decisions rather than emotional ones in pressure cooker situations.*

Due to the strict fitness regime we were subjected to, my weight bulked up as body fat turned into muscle. I might add that as a result, my jaw line took on the vague shape of a square and I was permitted to let my hair grow. The unconventional and optional afterhours sessions of cogitation (a form of thinking deeply) definitely made me assess situations better and I became more aware of my surroundings. The entire course gave me a renewed sense of purpose. *I went in as a young man and came out as a grown man.*

The overall training programme was intended to build our character in so many ways. We were trained to anticipate the unexpected and to overcome any adversity we would encounter in real-life situations and potentially hostile environments. Additionally, the strenuous exercises helped us discover our inner resourcefulness and our ability to improvise. Among the many lessons we learned, one haunting autumnal experience stands out. *Perhaps all along our trainers had intended to find out who would chicken-out…*

For this particular ordeal, one mid-summer night we assembled at midnight within the high security Royal Navy port in nearby Portsmouth. Not all the trainees were called to participate in this upcoming exercise. I was among the dozen lads who were selected. We boarded a mini-bus which then drove us down the hill to the harbour. We were led into a dimly-lit dressing room where frogman diving suits were hanging up on hooks. The planners must have already known our sizes because the tasking officer shouted out the designated hanger for each one of us. I was assigned number 6, the same number I wore in football. It then took ages to get into the various padded rubber skins that were provided for us. We needed to help each other to do so, especially during the cumbersome process of zipping up. I was the first to notice that no fins were furnished, only thick-layered neoprene socks that felt like boots.

Once we were all kitted and ready, it was no longer possible for me to identify any of my comrades. I could only see the eyes, as every other part of their body was covered from head to toe. Even without wearing flippers on our feet, our deportments were anything but graceful. As we filed out of the room we waddled like overweight penguins. No one had informed us ahead of time of the task ahead but we were advised to eat lightly for dinner. So, we were left to ponder the next stage. Obviously, a water-borne exercise was in store for us. Like a well-oiled machine, it had been meticulously planned. Nothing was left to chance. I could feel the collective trepidation kicking in. After a short shuffle to the dark dockside, we reached the underside of a grey monster towering over us. It was the bow of a large navy ship moored there. The craft could have been a frigate or a destroyer but certainly it wasn't a gunboat or a minesweeper. There was no name to be seen like commercial vessels usually display. She was sitting tall and proud in the water. Either it was a high tide or she was not fully laden or both. Standing there, in the windless night, we could see the stars twinkling directly above us. I could recognise the limp white St George's Ensign of the Royal Navy hanging way up on the ship's deck-side flagpole. However, the Union Jack on it was not visible to me from my position.

By now, other personnel were handing out scuba face masks and fitting small non-standard sized oxygen tanks onto our backs. I still couldn't figure out what it was we were going to be doing at all but clearly less weight to carry had been factored.

"Right, lads, listen up," said an older man in a uniform wearing a beret I had not seen before. His stern face reminded me of my school headmaster. His deep bass voice loomed out of the gloom, "what we are going to do is climb down that ladder there where the seaman is standing. At the bottom of the rungs waterside, you'll be greeted by another chap treading water who will guide you towards a submerged rope. What you have to do is grip that piece of string with your gloves like it's the last thing you will ever hold in your short miserable life. You'll abseil on the cord down the depths for about a full minute. Upon reaching the bottom, you'll no doubt sink in the muck. Your job is to keep holding on to that line and make your way underwater to the other end of this ship. Everyone got that? Any questions?"

Nobody spoke up. All hands stayed down. No intakes or outtakes of air heard.

He continued. "While you are down there, above you, you'll just about make out the bottom of the ship's hull. Its underwater sensors are switched off. The whole thing from start to finish will take you about half an hour, maybe a bit more. If you lose your grip and start floating off and/or get claustrophobia, panic or get stuck in a hole, be assured that the SBS (Special Boat Service) will come to your rescue. You may even just about make out those who look like seals swimming down there, so you all won't be alone. I assure you there are as many of them present as there are of you lot. If you come up to the back of somebody in front of you, gently tap him on the shoulder to indicate you want to pass him. Nobody can refuse the request. We don't want any bravado or demonstration of machoism. Just let him pass. This exercise is not going to be measured by how long or short it took you to perform it. It's all about completing the assignment. Depending on the results, I, in my role as the conducting officer will then tick a 'yes' or cross a 'no' on the report card with your name on it. No additional details will appear on the form of how many others you brilliantly overtook, etcetera. So no rush, take it easy. Go at your own comfortable pace to succeed.

"If you don't want to or can't continue, seen too many beckoning mermaids, all you have to do is wave your spare arm and hold it up. One of the fully-trained SBS divers down there will immediately come and safely escort you up and out of the water. Got that? Right then, starting from the left single file towards that man standing there dockside. He'll get you down that ladder one at a time. Good luck to you all."

I was blinking under my goggles and I even started to mildly hyperventilate. Bloody hell, this drill all sounded spooky to me. Certainly, they didn't give us any time to get frightened or to have second thoughts. On the positive side, the fact that we were all in here together as a group, helped confidence. I didn't hear any wisecracks or camaraderie as everybody was concentrating on the task ahead. Dread crept in slowly, definitely, but we had to overcome it. That was probably the whole idea behind this exercise. It was obviously designed to take us out of our comfort zone into the fear-of-god deep. *My old boarding school's headmaster's early advice echoed in my head, 'If you don't start with yourself, lad, you have already lost.'*

I was standing somewhere in the middle of the pack. When I got all the way down to where the sea bed was, I could barely see my hand in front of me, never mind the bloke who had gone down ahead of me. It's a massive shock to the system. In the blackness, I started my solo trudge and immediately sank knee-deep in some sludge that took much strength to extricate myself from. After this initial exertion, I needed time to recover and adapt to this new environment. To calm my mind, I began to think on ways to concentrate and save energy. Purposefully, I regulated my breathing and actions to slow mode. I was aware that objects in the water always looked bigger than usual and that my vision would eventually adjust to this strange anomaly. But that knowledge didn't help me in any way. There's nothing to see at all. It's another world, like sleeping with my eyes open.

For what seemed like several hours, I felt I was advancing at a snail's pace because I didn't catch up anybody ahead of me. A couple of times I looked back but saw no one behind me either. Just feeling that lifeline and holding onto it in my hands, gave me all the security I needed to keep moving forward to the end. Unquestionably, the going was hard and the current down there was so strong that it kept pushing and buffeting my body. I had to really grasp tightly on the hard-coiled thick twine to avoid from being pulled off and swept out to sea. But I persevered. At times, I felt a wave of wet sweat or whatever may be described as such. As fatigue seeped in, breathing became laboured and loud. I literally felt I was inside a tin can. I tried to block out these eerily unsettling images…after all, down here in these watery graveyards were the final resting places of many of the navy's war dead. I had no desire to join them yet! The mind plays some strange tricks…am I dreaming or is this real? Despite my attempt to control my emotions – sarcasm and anger took over. Not good, to simultaneously experience the two lowest forms of emotion. I began to suspect that the story about the SBS coming to the rescue was all BS and a ruse to lure us into a death trap. I certainly could not spot anything resembling a seal-like figure. Maybe I was imagining a floating seaweed. Besides, how could they see anybody waving their arms in distress, even if they were close by?

Suddenly and still in my state of semi-blindness, my neck jerked hard as my body smacked against a solid stone wall! At that exact moment, a character blowing bubbles came out of nowhere on my right and gave me a thumb's up signal. He grabbed my wrist roughly and wrestled my hand off the line I had been holding for dear life. At the same time, another diver on my left shoved me forcefully upwards. I ended up hitting my head for the second time with a loud clang against the bottom rung of another metal ladder. Despite feeling a mix of cramp, heartburn and pins and needles, I instinctively started to climb up. It was slow going. I think that last part was harder than the actual stagger along the sea bed as the suit was weighty and my legs had somewhat lost their full functionality. The water visibility slowly improved at this spot. At some point on the way up, while still submerged, I turned my head to look in the foggy distance. I could just about make out the stationary huge screws of the ship's propellers. When I eventually splashed through the water's surface, there was still much more work to do. It quickly got bloody chilly in the night air too. Right after the rush of adrenaline subsided, and the feeling of elation faded, the shivering cold kicked in and took over to neutralise any residual sense of exhilaration.

Finally, and after much effort, I reached the top of the rusty iron ladder. What I thought was a bright moon morphed into an unmoving solitary spotlight shining down from above a roof. I was a bit unsteady on my feet but strong hands held me up. Once again, I looked back at the ship's stern and I was in awe at the massive structure standing still in the faint light. Next, I simply stumbled in a haze to where the silent fingers were pointing me to go to.

As we dried ourselves in the stark dressing room, we were offered an invigorating cup of steaming hot milky tea. The mirror revealed I had a bruise on my forehead. It turned out that of the starting dozen who participated in this endurance course, four had drifted off course and two gave up the ghost. So, the success rate was 50-50. Did I feel proud of myself? Not really, because I was too knackered from the draining drill to even think. So was everybody else. And nobody engaged in celebratory high-fives or whooping. I think we were just happy to get the heck out of there. After taking off our diving gear, we all headed back up the hill to the fort. We took a quick hot shower and hit the sack. I was surprised I didn't have a nightmare for days afterwards, if I am honest. But that night, I slept soundly, even though we literally were thrown in the deep end.

That was one of many oddball endurance tests we had to undergo. The number in the class of those in contention to complete the course dwindled every week as the list of dropouts soared. I never befriended anybody really closely. I took the precaution of avoiding close interaction as I suspected that those seeking my friendship may have been assigned to pry information out of me. I didn't ask anybody about themselves either. It was a lonely time socially in that respect. Fortunately, I am okay with being by myself for long periods. I relied on my own way of meditation as well as tai chi. Much of those skills I owe to my unique upbringing growing up in Singapore and Hong Kong among the Chinese.

At around that time, those of us still remaining in the programme were introduced to the one-time pad and how to use it. It's an ingenious coding system first developed by the Soviets in the 1920's. It was later copied and significantly improved by the British and others. The one-time pad gets its name because it applies a new cipher for each message. Encryptions are never repeated, making it impossible for codebreakers to decipher the transmitted message.

Because I was also earmarked for fast-tracking to be a P (for production) officer, the extra training exercises towards the end of the 26 weeks at that SIS camp entailed some actual field work within the UK. Nearing the completion date, I was told that I would be assigned to the top secret Special Political Action section. SPA had been created in 1954 and was responsible for conducting covert action. In fact, the head of SPA had come down to Hampshire with his assistant to meet three of us in person. They drove all the way from Century House, SIS' then head office near central London, to brief us individually on what our objectives would be. I believe each of us was given a different task to perform but we did not discuss our specific assignment among ourselves. It was my first taste of how the compartmented world of SIS worked. Truthfully, I wasn't interested in what they had been told to do anyway. Instead, I intently focused on my own tasking order. To their credit, neither one of them asked me any probing questions either, even though we had opportunities aplenty to exchange information between us. But we all remained mum — probably because the main lesson, which had been drummed into us during our stay in Fort Monckton, was a saying among spies: *If more than one person knows a secret, it is no longer a secret.*

* * * * * * * * *

In October 1973, dressed in civilian attire and now sporting long hair, I attended the 72nd Annual Conference of the Labour Party in Blackpool, in the north of England, incognito on behalf of SPA. A month later, I made my way to Camden Town, north London, to cover the 33rd Congress of the Communist Party of Great Britain.

My instructions on both occasions, were to mill around the attendees and follow the proceedings. At the close of each gathering I was asked to tender a written report to the section head from the point of view of the nation's security and the overall future well-being of the country. "I need you to identify what fracture points (areas of tension) are worth exploiting. Pay attention to what pushes a group together and what pulls them apart," he'd said. I was too inexperienced to fully understand the ramifications of what he was asking me to do at the time. So, I simply nodded back in response to hide my political naiveté.

I was issued two registration badges. Both were under the same student name of Domenic Nash. No photo ID taken. Upon receipt, it occurred to me that somebody at SIS/SPA had a wry sense of humour because *Dom Nash* in Russian meant 'our home'. But then nobody other than a native from that part of the world would have known that, nor would have connected the proverbial dots.

I'd hoped I wouldn't run into my favourite uncle who, as far as I knew, was still an active union leader. But just before boarding the northbound train, I called my parents and my father informed me on the phone that his older brother had just retired. So that was settled and I avoided a potential chance meeting with my uncle.

At both meetings I stayed in a tiny cubicle at a modest family-run B&B, each time for two nights. A plate of heartburn (full English breakfast) was included in the price of the room, but I had to share the bathroom and loo. In each case the semi-detached houses were within walking distance of the respective assembly halls. It seemed that most other attendees I met had secured the same cheap accommodation arrangements as I did. I forced myself to partake socially in the local pubs in the evenings where there was more smoke cloud, than air. I later shared cheap take-out dinners consisting of tasteless lamb kebab or cardboard-like pepperoni pizza with my new boozy contacts. I mix quite well when I have to. Fortunately, I'm a light drinker. My hair and clothes reeked of tobacco in the mornings even though I don't smoke. After a positively busy weekend of action, I thought I could feel my arteries slowly hardening from all the bad food I'd digested!

People seem to copy each other while in a social environment. It is almost a universal human trait that I noticed almost immediately when engaged in group conversations. In this instance, quite a few people peppered their talk with a saying or two attributed to Joseph Stalin. One quote was, *'We must cultivate people as a gardener cultivates his favourite tree.'* I presumed it to be the in-slogan of the moment, which was a cool thing to mutter in new company. So, I did the same whenever the chance presented itself. *'We Communists have to pump ourselves full of knowledge,'* was the second most used phrase in such impromptu encounters, especially so later on in Camden. I reminded myself that what the SIS was in effect doing was grooming me and filling me with know-how of a different kind.

I became aware that catechism or repetition of the party line in lockstep uniformity, regardless of which side of the divide one follows, is mindless obedience to a lost cause. The real world doesn't work that way. The élite own the levers of society and believe that the rest of us are simply peons to serve them and satisfy their limitless greed. In truth, the world is not run by a duly elected government, but by the rich who cling fiercely to entrenched positions already in place from centuries ago. I reject this system wholeheartedly.

I also discovered very quickly that another dictum was prevalent in those circles. Four areas of the country were routinely referred to as *'Little Moscows'*. I actually hailed from one of them – the Tyne-Wear region. It was derived from the names of the two rivers that respectively flow through the city of Newcastle and Sunderland, my hometown. The other three regions were the Rhondda Valley in Wales; Glasgow, the largest city in Scotland; and East London, in the capital. All of these places traditionally leaned heavily to left wing causes.

I reckoned that the two gatherings would attract hundreds of shop stewards from branches of the trade unions as well as dyed-in-the-wool cloth-capped workers. I wasn't wrong. But I was rather surprised to see that many of the proletariat showed up as well. They belonged to the intellectual class and were easily recognisable by their Sunday best expensively-cut suits and silk ties, along with their posh and sophisticated accents. Back when I had studied for a year at Patrice Lumumba University in the Soviet Union, I had learned that according to the diehards, an integral part of the struggle of the international industrial working class was to shun such well-heeled people, as they were perceived by the true communists as either the privileged few or the landlord class. Was I looking at a faction once described by Togliatti (the founding member and leader of the Italian Communist party) as, *'not a right wing of the working class but a left wing of the bourgeoisie*? It was an interesting juxtaposition, with me looking at my own countrymen's mannerisms and assessing them all the way down to their dress-code!

The few seminars I went to seemed to attract the more militant elements of the activists. Old scores were being fought and settled openly. The quarrels got so heated at times that I expected punch-ups and fist fights to break out among the rabble-rousers. But those clashes never happened. Insults and threats were permissible and were often hurled with abandon. But coming to actual blows was what is known in Russian as *bespredelschik* (an off-limit).

Both in Blackpool and in London the *Handbook for Communist Party Members* were being widely distributed free. The CPGB (Communist Party of Great Britain) and the Labour Party had exhibition stalls at each other's proceedings. Perhaps they agreed to swap booths gratis to save themselves the fees.

The Labour Party leader, Harold Wilson, made the first major speech. Interestingly the very first issue he ranted on about related to a recent massacre of rebelling civilians in Mozambique committed by the Portuguese army. I certainly wasn't expecting to hear about this topic. Little did I know then that I would soon be paying a visit to Portugal on behalf of my employer…

In my duo of written reports on my observations from the conventions I attended, I didn't describe the working, the middle and the upper classes as such. Instead I respectively referred to them as the drinking underclass, the rank 'n' file tax-payers and the ruling class. Needless to say, the section head at the SIS' SPA was not amused nor impressed by my creative literary licence. A poker-faced older man he interestingly described my post-training exercises as the 'final scheme'. Later on, I found out that was the terminology used by the Special Operations Executive in World War II for recruits that had passed a practice mission after the completion of training. Back then, the SOE graduates were next sent to do the real thing. Likewise, I was about to begin my new career.

* * * * * * * * *

When I joined the SPA section proper at their office in SIS' London headquarters, I was truly astounded to discover the level of genuine hatred displayed by the senior officers towards those throughout the country who supported the 'hard left' or 'red menace within' or 'the great unwashed', as they labelled them. It was clear to me that the oft heard, *'It's the right thing to do'*, were code words for 'in the national interest'. It was a euphemism to justify and pursue interventionist or warlike policies. Plans were already in place to break up by force any strike called by the trade unions. Disruptions and confrontations were to be instigated by subversive elements and shadowy third parties (not yet known to me at the time). From what I could tell, the ultimate goal was to smash the labour movement and prevent it from gaining national solidarity. The quartet of impoverished regions in Britain, collectively known as Little Moscows, were also targeted for close attention by a government keen to replace them with 'entitlement' power for the benefit of the rich and the powerful.

As a junior intelligence officer at the time, I understandably kept a low profile, trying not to ruffle any feathers. But deep down I was profoundly bothered. As a teenager, I saw first-hand how my school friends and their families had suffered at the hands of the Conservative government then in power. PM Margaret Thatcher, its titular leader, unleashed the police on strikers and dissenters alike. They acted as her personal henchmen and broke up the coalminer's *work-to-rule* in the northeast of England. (Work-to-rule is an industrial action in which employees do no more than the minimum required by the rules of their contract. The action causes a slowdown, decreases productivity and reduces profit.) I had seen the pain, suffering and the deeply entrenched deprivation inflicted on the defenceless poor and the have-nots. There was no money for hot food and fuel for burning in fireplaces was no longer affordable. Even the monthly free bag of coal normally afforded to miners' families had been cut off. My parents frequently and kindly elected to feed the whole school football team in our house before matches were played.

Amid all that misery, the community at-large showed its true colours. Neighbours and workers from other industries, like the iron and steel, and dockyard workers, pitched in and shared their goodwill with their less fortunate brothers. In the end, no one was left out in the cold. But the cruel disenfranchisement of the lower classes and disproportionate enrichment of the upper capitalist tier, led to abject poverty among my friends and their families. Eventually, many of them emigrated to Australia, Canada, New Zealand, South Africa and the United States. Sadly, I never saw any of my school and college mates once I had transitioned to adulthood and joined the Royal Navy.

In retrospect, I realise that my life's lot was much more privileged than that of my mates from those days. I had spent much of my childhood (ages 1 to 12) in the sub-tropics of Asia, though I had gone to boarding school in County Durham from 7 to 12. From then on to adulthood (late-teens), I continuously lived in the northeast of England. Given the environment I grew up in, I acquired a rather indistinct accent that was regarded by many, as neutral. When people heard me talking, they could not immediately place me as being from anywhere in particular, though they were confident I was British. I was neither poor nor rich. In Britain, local citizens routinely made assumptions on your background and class the moment you opened your mouth and uttered a sentence or two. In my own case, I was able to get through the subconscious barriers that exist in all walks of British society. I felt equally at ease in the rust belt or political gatherings as I was at the SIS' offices or the haloed halls of government ministries. In short, I felt I integrated well at both ends of the social spectrum.

My loss of innocence was slow and gradual. Up to then, to me, truth was a multilayer concept that made the world run on the right track in the years that would follow. The transformation began soon after I made several trips to hand-deliver and pick-up reports to and from the SIS office and Palace of Westminster (the meeting place of the House of Commons and the House of Lords). The notion that the civil servants are supposed to be the guardians of impartiality, proved to be just a trick and a mirage. Members of Parliament (MP's) belonging to the Conservative, Labour or Liberal (later Liberal Democrat) Parties are elected by us to carry out our collective wishes. (Green, UKIP, Momentum and Independent came much later.) But it really didn't matter which political party was voted in, as the mandarins (the nickname given to senior civil servants) ran the show behind closed doors. You have to spend time with these personae to see how the system really works. Their sense of entitlement is galling to the average person. These are the bureaucrats and decision-makers who actually control the inner workings of the government. Their approach is to appoint their caddies to key positions in all decision-making circles in government. In this way, they are able to influence policy on behalf of their paymasters in the Establishment. It's a strategy of encroachment that works well for defenders of the realm. Little could be done to advance an agenda without the acquiescence of the mandarins in charge. Even worse, these non-elected functionaries had the power to initiate actions that were against the public good.

When SIS assessments or requests for action from the field landed in the inbox tray, the section head had complete discretion on their ultimate fate. The secretary would physically place them where he or she deemed they belonged: put them in the left file or right file, chuck them in a rubbish bin, or even shred the contents altogether. By the same token, he could route them to relevant individuals, prioritise them for further action or bury them in an out-of-the way drawer never to see the light of day again. The same principles applied when making and scheduling appointments in person. The mandarins answered *only* to their masters in the Establishment and the ruling class. Even instruments of law and policy were drafted discreetly, a key word changed here and there, then presented for signatures by busy ministers. Meanwhile, behind closed doors the administrators spoke about elected representatives in such a way that made it sound like they were indigent slaves to the system. The interests of the public at large were rarely factored into the equation. All in all, they were really good at keeping themselves out of the limelight and operating beneath the radar.

Those few in the know were left to bemoan this betrayal of moral and intellectual responsibility to the general public. It came to be known as *la trahison des clercs Britanique* (the treason of British bureaucrats). The term was borrowed from the title of a book published in 1927 by the French philosopher Julien Benda.

Back at SIS' SPA in the early days, I wasn't yet privy to the identity of the agent provocateurs tasked with the dark arts of breaking up the strikes and causing mayhem. But I soon found out who these bad actors were. Within a few months, I was astounded to confidentially learn first-hand the broad details of a fascist game plan to subvert and disrupt the unionised UK labour movement. The government through its security agencies, had got into bed with organised crime to do their dirty work for them and execute the nefarious plot of weakening the labour movement and the civil rights struggle. The Security Service, otherwise known as MI5, handled domestic liaisons. It created a new section that secretly met with select East London-based gangsters whose domain had dwindled due to long-term imprisonment. Meanwhile my own SIS section was assigned to collude with various mafias overseas. We coordinated our plots at the London Controlling Station (both MI5 and SIS/MI6). It was really a joint unit responsible for spreading rumours, disinformation and deception with the specific aim of disrupting the legitimate activities of the trade unions. This behind-the-scene group was also tasked with fulfilling the so-called 'production' requirements. In all instances, the unit cynically engaged in event-shaping. It was all done through back-channels and by 'certain arrangements' (mandarin-speak for the secret services). Naturally, the mob wasn't going to do the job for nothing. They needed a substantial pay-off to first besmirch and then ruin the unions using what was described as the 'counter-gangs method' (defined as a task to deliberately provoke a reaction to then justify a response).

Unbelievably the proxy marriage-made-in-hell was greenlighted by those governing us! At the time, the Italian-American author Mario Puzo had his *The Godfather* books selling in Britain, and the movie of the same name was also a box office hit in the cinemas. I don't know if the powers that be were swayed by the so-called romanticism of the silver screen, but the general elections were rapidly approaching. My young mind thought the negative action was an unwise move to win votes and to cling to power. Clearly the plot wasn't going to end well. The steady erosion of the trust in those meant to lead the public reached a critical juncture. During this period, it was clear the people were being treated as a commodity, rather than flesh and blood with a brain, tongue and emotions.

The various terminology used in the right-wing press to describe the labour unions, was meant to paint them as the ugly side and elicit revulsion within the public. These anti-left papers were filled with dispatches on football hooliganism, yobbos, drug dealers, burglars, fanatics and anarchists. All were supposedly unemployed and enjoying benefits (dole). The list was long. Hiding behind sham pretexts, these power-grabbers unleashed secretly paid home-grown louts as well as imported goons to implement this ugly scheme. The hired guns methodically singled out British trade unionists for special treatment. What that unverified skulduggery entailed, I could only imagine. During that period, no detailed reports ever appeared in the intellectual media except for the lone fact that there was a steep rise in 999 emergency calls to the police. The boys in blue dealt with a multitude of common assaults, overdoses, car accidents, a variety of break-ins and many other unexplained incidents. Black markets were created almost overnight. Gangster capitalism brutally exploited the British public for exorbitant gain. Even small bombs were planted to implicate known terrorist organisations and falsely pin the blame on them.

Obviously, those who orchestrated the activities to alter a political destiny, would steadfastly deny any such plot ever existed. So, no folders were ever created to detail the rapidly evolving scheme. Being privy to this level of monkey business put a strain on me. I wasn't sleeping well. The head-on collision between knowledge and my moral duty deeply unsettled me. It was not what I thought we should be doing. To my mind, we were worse than the criminals. I was thinking of quitting.

* * * * * * * * *

The job of the citizen is to keep his mouth open.
– Günter Grass, German writer, 1927-2015

Then, much to my surprise and against all odds an end-point was reached. In early 1974 Harold Wilson of the Labour Party was voted into power by the people of Britain! To the dismay of the top brass at SIS, he had ousted the incumbent – the Conservative Edward Heath. The dastardly game plan had backfired spectacularly!

In his first few days as Prime Minister, Wilson convened his cabinet and must have informed them what the security agencies had evidently been instructed to do in the run-up to the elections. I knew this because the SPA section of the SIS, which had been operational for 20 years, was disbanded overnight and immediately ceased to exist. I have no direct knowledge of the fate of the senior fellows. I know I never crossed paths with any of them again. Besides, since so much is compartmented at SIS, I would never know. But we younger officers were at once transferred to other sections. The one I was assigned to next, to this day, has not been identified publicly – so I cannot divulge its name. Because I understood Russian, I was mostly assigned to duties pertaining to the Sovbloc (Soviet Union and its Eastern European satellites, also known as the Warsaw Pact countries).

I know my story about this omnishambles is not remotely in the mainstream but nor is my kind of work. Certainly, it was a string of blunders and miscalculations performed by arrogant people who thought they were above the law. I herein confirm this disclosure is true but I cannot prove its authenticity. But much like nothing being put down in writing in files back then, the scheme isn't meant to be for public consumption even 45 years on. Nor can it be declassified because the details were not classified to start with. Such is how certain operations at SIS were conducted at the beginning of my career.

In the cold war SIS' secret operations, especially overseas, had no oversight by any UK democratic institution for the simple fact it would run into a fundamental contradiction of its purpose. Almost everything SIS' special operations did constituted a breach of the laws of other countries, as the type of activity it conducted across borders was not possible to circumscribe within the framework of legislation. *So any covert action was designed as plausibly deniable.*

It is time that the conventional practice of maintaining silence for fear of upsetting the apple cart and the nefarious spreading of disinformation in the UK, ceases at once. The hard-working citizenry deserve the truth and honest accounting of the government's activities. The public is finally getting wise to the repeated use of smear tactics by politicians of all stripes to create a smokescreen for their misdeeds and advance their self-centred agenda. In small but meaningful ways, the people are demanding change. Interestingly enough, the same trends are now occurring in many other developed countries.

In the aftermath of this sordid episode, the accelerated economic development (*uskoreniye* in Russian) that followed, opened the door for three groups from the Russian underworld to import their criminal networks into the British Isles. Politically savvy, these characters of questionable integrity created a wide range of shady business entities. They got involved in investments and high-interest loans, close protection security, debt collection and arms deals. They set up high-end prostitution rings and created channels for illegal distribution of cigarettes and other tobacco products. They also claimed hashish, khat, cannabis and marijuana grown in their 'stans' (republics of the Soviet Union with names ending in stan) as their exclusive share of the drug trade.

To a lesser degree, several Italian mobs also entered the fray and positioned themselves so as to benefit from lucrative criminal activities. They demanded and received kickbacks from construction projects, controlled the ports, racketeering/extortion, undertakers/funeral parlours, overpriced car parks and exorbitant industrial cleaning contracts. Cocaine distribution was also their gig.

Fourteen Hong Kong Triads, the largest of which was Wo On Lok (also known as Water Room), were already active in London in a small way, slowly encroaching on the depleted British enforcers territories. They too expanded their operations and significantly increased their revenue streams. In particular, they set up gambling dens in basements as well as cheap brothels above nail salons and Chinese food restaurants, often within the same building. In return for the freedom to unhindered operation of their opium and heroin business, and involvement in human trafficking, these gangs had agreed to have all their locations wiretapped from top to bottom (by the police and MI5). To circumvent this reluctantly agreed intrusion, they often rented new places without informing the authorities.

Despite losing ground in their respective homelands as a result of clampdowns by the Soviet Union, Italy and Hong Kong, all the aforementioned groups actively participated in the secret war to disrupt and crush the unions in Britain, during the eventful period of 1973-1974. The covert activities involved paid goons who singled out striking union members for *a whacking* (their words) if their threats were ignored. How effective such tactics of intimidation were, is unknown to me. The British authorities wilfully turned a blind eye to all these illegal activities in return for 'services rendered' in busting the labour movement across the country. But, interestingly, the activities never extended to assassination or murder of British citizens. A line of patriotism was drawn there, not to be crossed. The profits generated from the illicit underground economy stayed in the City of London financial district. Nevertheless, substantial cash deposits were also diverted to multiple offshore tax havens. These transfers were all approved by the chess players at the top of the British establishment. As a result, London is now openly the 'dirty money' (corrupt assets) capital of the world, while the UK is the cocaine use capital of the world.

To this day, the *vory-v-zakone* operating on the streets (in Russian it means men who follow the code, but it loosely translates to thieves-in-law), are dominated by the Moscow Kingiseppskaya gang. It is named after a village called Kingisepp near the Estonian border that was a scene of a WWII battle between the victorious Red Army and the defeated Nazis. The term *skaya* means belonging to.

The Italian mobsters were mainly represented by 'Ndrangheta. It was a low-profile confederation of 80+ Calabrian families who controlled the province of Calabria, situated halfway between the better-known Neapolitan and Sicilian regions of southern Italy. The name itself is derived from the Greek words for heroism, loyalty and virtue. Along with the Russian gangs, the Italian mobsters are by far the biggest criminal enterprises currently in operation in Britain. Some of their dealings are still unregulated. Others, however, have evolved over time. They have since spread their tentacles to become legitimate businesses. The low-level knife-wielding street delinquents today trading in small doses of narcotic hits in Britain don't know who their ultimate masters are.

It should be noted that despite their Russian origins, the Vory were openly defiant of communism and Soviet rule. With the collapse of the USSR and the rise of the new Russia from the ashes, these groups were perfectly placed to seize control of the emerging opportunities to enrich themselves. Many bosses from the fraternity are nowadays known as the oligarchy (taken from the Greek word *oligarkhia* meaning government by the few). Furthermore, the 'Russians' today are not necessarily ethnic

Russians. Many associates of this new ruling class actually hail from Georgia and Latvia (former republics of the Soviet Union). They make up large percentages of this elite club. It should be noted that Kingiseppskaya (and Tambovskaya from St Petersburg) as well as 'Ndrangheta (and the Naples-based Camorra) have deep-seated antipathy towards homosexuality. They are also very religious. The Russian gangs are Orthodox while their Italian partners in crime are Roman Catholic. Sometimes they pool their talents depending on the nature of the new project and on the potential rewards. In the permissive business environment of the UK, white collar crime is evidently acceptable.

Mafia and states are similar beasts. They both impose governance on people. They claim control of a territory where individuals reside, and want to impose order. When mafias operate within a state's borders, they have negotiated a pact that allows them a degree of autonomy. Politicians 'share power' with the criminal organisation…

– Federico Varese, author, *Mafia Life*

The mistaken thinking back then was that *the enemy of one's enemy is one's friend*. It was the colossal naivety and stupidity of the British government that allowed ochlocracy (mob rule) from distant lands to get its foot in the door and set up shop in the UK, to the detriment of the law-abiding citizenry. As for the British leaders responsible for this massive failure, it was all about maintaining power, covering themselves with undeserved glory and gaining prestige. For the hard boys sanctioned to try and eliminate socialism, it was about making lots of easy, unlimited, untraceable cash and transferring it out of the country without paying any taxes.

The people who govern us haven't fooled themselves but they have fooled us, the people. Sadly, this inconvenient truth has become a vicious and never-ending cycle evolving into 'dark money', which is bestowing funds by unknown donors to non-profits, who then secretly influence elections via lobbying. Our democracy was sold out a long time ago.

As a result of this botched affair, I haven't been able to spell government with a capital G since. Despite my services to Queen and country I also think I'm on the losing side. The prevailing gangster-style capitalism and the rampant spread of the millions of new immigrants who have failed to assimilate into British life are the reasons for my conclusion. But that's another story.

Each of us can be guilty of not speaking up. Well I have now because nobody else did.

Those who have the privilege to know have the duty to act.

– Albert Einstein

* * * * * * * * *

Chapter One

When ideas are neglected by those who ought to attend to them...they often acquire an unchecked momentum and an irresistible power over multitudes of men that may grow too violent to be affected by rational criticism.

– Isaiah Berlin, theorist and philosopher (1909-1997)

Upon the closure on the Special Political Action unit, I was transferred to another Secret Intelligence Service sub-division in the same London head office building. The new section dealt with all things to do with the Soviet bloc. Before long, my new head decided to send me in late-April 1974 on my first overseas jaunt. At the ripe age of 23, I was dispatched on my maiden *solo* assignment to Lisbon, the capital of Portugal, which confused me as it was nowhere near the Soviet Union. I was 'to learn on the job and to report on events that were shaping up over there', as my boss put it.

It was not long after I 'celebrated' my alive day (in military jargon the term refers to the date one nearly died in combat.) In my case, almost a year to the day since I was shot down while flying a Royal Navy helicopter on a secret operation in Laos. I survived the crash and the ensuing ground enemy fire. I also needed a cold-blooded presence of mind to prevail over a lone enemy combatant determined to end my life. I am alive today to recount the story but I sustained lifelong injuries that still afflict me to this day.

Just before my send off, my immediate supervisor briefed me further on the upcoming assignment. No tradecraft or codenames would be required, only standard prefatory protocol. I was instructed to meet up with a local contact and to report back on what the Portuguese man had to say. As a cover, I was provided with a badge, this time with a photo that identified me as a newly-hired junior reporter for a London-based daily newspaper with a small special interest circulation. To my amazement, I later found out that the paper was known to be directly funded by the Communist Party in Moscow. I naturally assumed the rag knew nothing about me nor about the temporary fake press pass I was issued. It seemed it was only going to be used for a few days to serve some unknown and elusive purpose.

I would have rightfully thought the tasking order was a training exercise meant to help me process the cognitive aspects of becoming a full-fledged intelligence officer. A fellow junior SIS officer who had progressed with me from the same class, upon learning of my imminent trip, half-jokingly advised me in class-speak: "Remember, this means you must pay attention to spoken discourse markers, filled pauses and weasel-type swerve words in English uttered by foreigners. And don't forget the probability of a proposition's truth is determined by the incremental accumulation of evidence. Good luck!" Well it was true. I didn't speak Portuguese then and I still don't now! But reflecting on the events back then, I can only assume that those few in the know in my new section at SIS must have known something was brewing in that country which wasn't yet public. After all, they were in charge of knowing what was going on behind the Iron Curtain and yet Portugal was in the exact opposite geographical direction. But I was still too much of an underling in the pecking order to point out this anomaly to the briefing officer, so I stayed mum.

I left on a weekday and my line officer/handler had said that he expected me to be back in the office in London in time for the start of the following week. He then added he had some other job in mind for me to undertake in Poland. Though the task was deemed then as routine, to gain experience, *it was far from it*. His parting words were, "The first big plank to nail down, *if* you discover that the person you are liaising with is a usable source, then you need to determine if he is credible, then verifiable, with no caveats stripped out."

With his cautionary words still ringing in my ears, I spent time perusing the day's print media prominently displayed at the newsstand in the airport departure lounge. I was hoping to get into the 'feel' of being a journalist for a few days. Our instructors at SIS had taught us that the media were the lie factories that actually disseminated and promoted the agendas of the political and industrial élite (even though those who wanted to disclose the untruths were lawfully restricted from doing so by the Official Secrets Act, D-Notices and other censorship devises). Considering that premise, this undertaking felt somewhat ironic considering I had false ID. After skimming through a couple of papers, I detected nothing that was going down in the Iberian Peninsula, at least not in English buzzwords. I consoled myself by remembering reading a public inquiry report just before graduating SIS training where the Director General of the Security Service (head of MI5) had been quoted as saying that "90% of what he reads in newspapers is inaccurate".

But as I have grown older and wiser, I am now increasingly aware of the ways that myths gradually evolve into 'facts' through subtle manipulation by the fourth estate (press) in general. I have also found that most reporters compose in the same distinctive style universally taught at schools of journalism. It is also well known that traditional columnists disdain authors who use the word 'I' or write in the first person. As time has gone by, the news has become tightly bound by the rules of political correctness, so much so that correspondents cannot say or write what they want to anymore. It's not a medium where information is gleaned from, rather the public prefers outlets that tells them what they want to hear or read.

My British European Airways (BEA) flight took me from Heathrow directly into Lisbon's international airport. Everything seemed normal in the arrival terminal as I collected my bag from the carousel. I elected to take the cheap nonstop bus into the city centre. After the 25-minute ride, as instructed, I checked into a pre-booked backstreet inexpensive hostel in the old town. I did a routine check for bugs as I was taught to, then headed straight out to get a handle on what was supposed to be going on – if anything. I immersed myself in the new environment as the SIS called it.

The people I came across were going about their usual business and did not seem particularly preoccupied with anything of political significance or otherwise. When I got back into my room, I turned on my TV to the local news. Nothing in the broadcast suggested any imminent disturbance in the making. I detected nothing that could remotely point to a ripple effect…at least on the surface of things. I admit I felt as if I was on a well-deserved break. Upon my return from south-east Asia I had attended many hospital appointments and then spent six months of continuous tutoring at the two SIS schools for spies. I felt I fully deserved a holiday.

After half a day out and about in Lisbon, I treated myself that evening to a beer and ate delicious tapas food in an ancient-looking bar down the street from my hostel. The place was also where I was to meet the local contact. Since I was early, I played the role of an English tourist and got into some pleasant chats with people around me. The local inebriate next to me, I remember in his stupor, slurped in English, "Not to know beer is not normal." It made me chuckle into mine. Drunks are such breathtakingly dull fellows, generally. But the conversations revealed nothing of importance, other than apparently some songs that were previously banned were now being played on national radio. That titbit of information went over my head at the time but looking back, it signified a crucial change was coming down the pipeline in their society. I was thinking at that moment in time that any article in newsprint I would have tendered as a reporter, would have ended up as a short item hidden away in some back pages.

After about half an hour of idle waiting, the genial barman who had previously served me, opened up a conversation. He introduced himself in English as Gonzalo and proceeded to engage me in small talk. At the end of a comment on a coach for the football club, Sporting Lisbon, he deftly veered the conversation. He shrugged animatedly while using a saying by Trotsky to stress that things were as good as could be (as related to the football club). "Combined and uneven developments," he had uttered glibly after a slight hesitation. *That* was the introductory code phrase I was waiting for!

I responded, as I was supposed to, with the closing code phrase, "It's funny what a difference a day in the life can make." We both smiled and locked our eyes on each other. He then moved off to serve another customer. I had no idea the barman was the person I was waiting for!

Frankly, I was expecting an older man but he was about my age. All along I was thinking it would be another patron, sitting on the stools at the bar like I was.

Several minutes later, he stopped by again where I sat at the bar. He briefly asked me to meet him outside the bar the next morning at 9 AM. I nodded in acceptance. Before I left the establishment, I paid him the bill and gave him a tip. All the while, we were careful to avoid any hint that we had made contact a short time earlier. We both maintained our professional poker faces.

The next morning, I was awoken at dawn by the loud sound of gunfire evidently emanating from a nearby location. Being originally from the armed forces and prepared, my next day's clothes were ready to throw on. I quickly ran out onto the streets to find out what the disturbance was all about. Standing there it felt like the area was hit by an earthquake. The earth below and the pavement were vibrating under my feet. I heard the rumble of heavy tanks and saw them rolling along the main street one block over. Some soldiers in uniform were running alongside the moving armoury in crouching protection mode. What the heck was going on?

A small rabble with their fists clenched in the air ran by shouting fervently, *"Revolução! Revolução!"* A revolution was in progress! No shit! It certainly didn't feel like one. The spectacle had a carnival party feel to it.

The next thing I knew, Gonzalo was running down the cobblestone street towards me, with his hair all dishevelled. Seconds later, he was beside me slightly out of breath. "This is definitely an uneven development," I grinned.

He quickly pulled me away out of any possible line of fire and ushered me into a nearby old-fashioned café. Sitting down just inside the doorway he chortled, "We are meeting here earlier than expected. Even an hour can make a difference. You know, yesterday, at my alcoholics' workplace, you were the *third* person I muttered that opening line to. The others just looked at me dumbly!"

I responded with a lesson learned from SIS' school for would-be intel officers, "Read the room, take in the vibes and let it all filter out. It's no different to crystal ball gazing in a bar full of strangers." It made Gonzalo laugh inwardly.

While we waited for service, I was to quickly learn that he was a fully-paid up member of the Portuguese Communist Party. He proudly showed me his laminated card displaying his murky photo and name. He looked like a teenager locked in the frame. I reciprocated by taking out my press card and offering it for his perusal. It displayed my own photo and my assumed name.

After the coffee was served, I waited for him to tell me what I was there for.

"For me there will be no more studying of creative poverty. Today, Alastair, the stupidly arrogant Salazarist dictatorship will finally be over. They have been in power since the 1930's, all my young life and yours. We, the people, have willed change and it has finally arrived. We have much to celebrate but still much more work is needed to put all this into motion."

"Okay, so what is it you want to relate to my organisation?" I replied. I naively assumed he knew who I really represented.

He looked into me at length while I sat still holding his eyes. "You are a very intense person I see, as I am. The information isn't anything that is happening today but it will be happening tomorrow. Tomorrow being anytime in the next 12 months. And it is of big importance to the world. *The Plan.*" His eyes sparkled when he said The Plan.

I didn't say anything but gave him a look that prompted him to continue. I couldn't make him out until he told me what the punchline would be. The racket outside was getting louder by the minute as more rejoicing citizens took to the streets. Nor did I think I was 'intense' but I let it go. The training instructor had said that foreigners tended to misread the British as appearing unconcerned when we are actually deep in concentration.

It turned out Gonzalo was born in Angola of Portuguese parents. He'd gone back to Africa every year as an adult and had many friends there. Some of them even had some clout in the local political scene in the Angolan capital, Luanda. Portugal was its colonial master. Its empire included Cape Verde Islands, Guinea-Bissau, Macao, Mozambique and São Tomé & Principe. He claimed the Portuguese language had the biggest difference in the world between the number of speakers in its homeland to those living abroad. And when queried by me what it was, his answer was "20 times 10 million, thus 200 million". It was a new one to me. I had always thought more spoke English outside of England. I ended the topic on, "Well, I *do* know 100,000 speak Esperanto and that it was invented in Poland." It brought a smile from my Portuguese friend.

"But Angola is the key to the future. The country is rich in natural resources, particularly gas, precious metals and minerals. Do you see what I am leading up to?"

"Only if you spell it out for an idiot like me," I replied with a grin. We seemed to be getting along quite well. Both of us almost the same age, of similar build and long hair, too.

We ordered another coffee each and some delicious pastry for breakfast.

"The three independence movements in Angola that have confronted the colonial power over the past decades will now start to fight among themselves. The one who wins will one day control billions in revenue…"

I was starting to see where he was going now. "So, how does that concern anybody where I am from?"

"You will understand the picture I am painting eventually, Alastair, I'm sure," he predicted. We did eye tennis out of the café's window at a screaming mob that came by waving national flags, followed down the narrow street by another bunch with red flowers. "In order to succeed, the various independence parties of Angola will need much weaponry. The one with the most firepower will win the spoils. And the supplier of the equipment to the winner will be amply rewarded for having helped the cause with billions in revenue, hopefully going towards socialist causes globally. You have been in the English military, no?"

"Yes, I was in the British armed forces until not long ago. I was involved in Laos, next door to where the Americans were fighting the war in Vietnam. I have seen war from close-up. Okay, so what is it you want me to do for you?"

"I am a committed Marxist. I have been affiliated to the Communist Party of Angola for a long time…"

I interrupted him. "My country isn't Communist. We actively fight against Communism, at least on the surface of things. I went to university in Moscow for one year and I see both sides of the coin. However, the British government will not support your cause. They will more than likely support a pro-West faction. But I am happy submit a detailed report in writing spelling out what you are saying though, if you feel it will help you."

My statement seemed to stump him momentarily, and he slumped into his seat while staring outside at the middle distance towards another crowd of people shouting. Thank goodness for the diversionary background noise caused by the proletariat just a few yards away on the other side of the juddering thin pane of glass. It gave me time to figure out where this cooperation was going and what was the underlying reason for our link-up. Was I in danger myself? We could hear shots being fired outside, not far away. But I think the bullets may have been aimed upwards into the air, based on the sound heard.

"But you will write an article, a report you say, about what is happening here in your newspaper?"

I realised there and then that he didn't know I was in the SIS. He actually thought I was a writer for a red British newspaper. Of course he did, it was my cover. Stupid me! Moments earlier, I had almost put my foot in my mouth and revealed to him I was in the SIS. A brief memory of a training exercise devised by SIS' conducting officers (trainers) a few months ago flashed in front of me: Aboard a commercial plane flight to the Mediterranean, where unknown to us trainees the attractive young woman sitting next to each of us was from the Royal Air Force – but in plainclothes. They had been instructed to chat us up and find out what we did for a living and where we were travelling to. I was one of three out of 18 who didn't succumb to the temptation to impress. I got around the issue by falling asleep instead – and the sexy Welsh girl was a bit of a corker, too!

I snapped out of my cold sweat into the present. "Of course, I can file it within hours when I get home. Seeing it is unlikely a telex office will be open now, I have an open airline ticket to return when I want to."

That seemed to perk him up. What a cock-up that would have been, Anderson, I was saying to myself, as I assented to his query with a smirk of relief.

So Gonzalo told me what The Plan was, lock stock and barrel, hoping to get global press coverage. It was a blueprint for the future of the red collectivists in black Africa.

A trio of parties active in Angola would soon start fighting among themselves to gain power. First among them was the Marxist Popular Movement for the Liberation of Angola, known as the MPLA, to whom Gonzalo fervently belonged. Apparently, he knew some honchos in the hierarchy well. The FNLA, which stood for National Front for the Liberation of Angola and The National Union for the Independence of Angola (UNITA) were the two other groups vying for control. I scribbled the info all down in the used notepad I was issued the day before. Gonzalo spoke about many topics and I wrote down absolutely everything he verbalised in long-hand. Screw it if he noticed I didn't do short-hand.

At the end of his talk, I posed some questions. We exchanged details on how we could get in touch with each other again, and bade farewell with a brotherly hug. I considered my reason for coming to Portugal over. Barging my way through the jostling herd blocking me, I made my way across the road to my hostel, packed up my few belongings, and headed to Lisbon airport. As the buses had been cancelled, it took a while to find a taxi but eventually I hailed one. On the drive out, more and more people were taking to the streets, excitedly, but not in an extremely violent way – though some mosh pits battles ensued. Physical incidents would increase throughout the day before it got better.

* * * * * * * * *

A rather funny sequence happened en route to Lisbon Airport. Things started to go a bit haywire when the animated taxi driver learned I was flying to London. He explained to me that because of the unexpected revolution, the workers at Heathrow Airport had gone out on strike in sympathy with their comrades in Portugal. I had no way of knowing if that was true or not, but that was what he said. Sure enough, BEA's check-in desk was closed. I was directed by a helpful girl in a uniform to the Sabena counter, the then national airline of Belgium. The Sabena ground crew confirmed that BEA had indeed stopped flying because of a lightning strike. I and a dozen other passengers were rebooked to fly to Brussels and connect on a London-bound Sabena flight. No problem as far I was concerned. The airport terminal was empty and peaceful compared to the shrieking hoards downtown. I even could hear my footsteps walking.

About 90 minutes later while I was sitting on the Sabena plane, I noticed from my port-side window a BEA Trident pulling in next to us. A minute later the captain announced that everybody originally scheduled for London should immediately disembark and board the BEA aircraft. I did as instructed.

As we were walking across the tarmac, I was the only passenger that remarked about my bag being on the wrong plane. Nobody seemed overly concerned, since they all wanted to get out of a country in the throes of a rebellion and before it got out of control. I was assured that all luggage originally bound for England would be there upon our arrival. It didn't make sense to me, since international security regulations usually require baggage to be loaded on the same flight as the passengers.

Just as we were seated on the British plane, the cabin crew announced yet another change. We were told that the strike in the UK was back on and that we were going to fly south to Morocco next to pick up additional passengers stranded in Tangier and Casablanca.

Strangely enough, once in North Africa and after an hour sitting in the still oppressive heat of the dying day at Casablanca airport, we were advised of an overnight layover in North Africa. We were issued with a BEA small overnight package of necessities.

Next, after a lovely dinner at the luxury hotel we were put up in, I decided to go for a walk on the beach alone. I wanted to assimilate all that Gonzalo had talked to me about. What happened in that wee walk turned out to be an amazing encounter I would never forget. In a flash, a giant of a camel swiftly ran out of the darkness and painfully bit my arm, giving me quite a fright! I had to run into the sea knee-deep to escape a further attack, where I next worried about my plasma attracting predators that swam.

Eventually I managed to wade to the welcoming light of the hotel further along the beach. Soaking wet, I had blood pouring from my elbow where the animal had taken a lump out of me. The reception staff called a doctor and ten minutes later I was being cleaned up by a professional wearing a white coat in a back room. I suffered the indignity of an inoculation in my backside to prevent rabies from the wound. During the examination the Moroccan medic had enquired, in passing, about how and where the incident had happened. So, I told him exactly what had transpired. His response blew me away, "Oh, that camel."

I remarked words to the effect that this camel apparently had bitten people before and he confirmed it was so. I laugh about it now, when I think about the incident! The camel had a history of chewing on unsuspecting humans and nobody had bothered to do anything about prevention of further attacks! Welcome to how things went down in Morocco! From the deepest recesses of my mind I never expected this kind of occurrence on the same day as being caught in an uprising! Seemed that things happened to me in pairs, not threes!

Anyhow I arrived in my own country a day later than expected, in much discomfort, my arm still in a sling. I went straight to SIS' office in Century House, a few minutes' walk from Lambeth North tube. To my utter dismay – my boss in that slightly insouciant demeanour which educated Englishman of a certain standing project – failed to commiserate with me about having stumbled into an insurrection, nor about my clear-to-see excruciating injury. He instead muttered with a serious face, "What took you so long?" I was to hear this remark often in my career, but that was the first time. It's what bored and patronising office people at the SIS say about busy field operators in an attempt to annoy them. I accept full well now that compliments will never come from such personae. Nor am I the kind of personality that attracts sympathy, it seems.

Despite lots of the staff taking good-humoured piss out of me for having being chomped on by a rabid camel and that Sabena stood for 'Such A Bad Experience Never Again', I went on to work for SIS on and off for almost two decades.

But let me please return to what happened in Angola. I duly wrote my situation report for SIS and it was filed away. To the best of my knowledge, no initial official action was taken by the British government ministry. I wasn't in the least surprised. Most certainly no article ever appeared in the local workers press by me. However, the BBC broadcast a lengthy bulletin about the 'disruption' in Portugal. A few days later, the news moved onto other current affairs. It also turned out the lightning strike by BEA 'allegedly' had no connection whatsoever to the events taking place in Portugal. While the UK was struggling with various industrial actions and a crippling three-day work week, it was the kind of psychobabble one hears the world over when the chaos of the moment arrives and when crazy things are going on around them. In such instances people talk irrationally and become unthinkingly opinionated over others, just to add worthless gossip to the unfolding drama.

* * * * * * * * *

By using covert means to underpin a broader conventional position, Britain sought to preserve influence and an illusion of power.

> – Rory Cormac, *Disrupt and Deny: Spies, Special Forces,*
> *and the Secret Pursuit of British Foreign Policy*

Every year since that fateful day in 1974, Freedom Day is now celebrated in Portugal and its former colonies on 25 of April. I feel exalted to this day to have witnessed a relatively peaceful revolt in the making.

The first created SIS file on the subject matter was marked: Revolution of the Flowers. But in Portuguese it was *Revolução dos Cravos*, so the folder was later renamed The Carnation Revolution.

Between 4 and 6 innocent victims of a complicated game were reportedly killed in Lisbon during the short-lived upheaval.

In order to avoid a civil war in Angola, nine months later in January 1975 the new Portuguese government pre-emptively announced the date of the future independence of the African nation for 11 November 1975.

As a result, a proxy war kicked off between the MPLA, the FNLA and UNITA. Gonzalo's political choice, the MPLA, won hands-down – probably because they had a head-start due to their members having foresight. The Cubans admirably sent a whole army and transported much equipment thousands of miles on behalf of the Soviets to support the MPLA's endeavours. American funds and a few Yankee advisors got behind UNITA efforts in their ultimate defeat. I'm not sure who backed the FNLA. Socialism won over capitalism in this instance. Undetermined numbers of blameless civilians and soldiers lost their lives. Certainly, in the hundreds of thousands.

What I do know is that because my own country didn't act humanitarianly or use soft power when it should have, the UK later applied spoilsport overt commercial sanctions on the Angolan people who took the brunt of the economic measures. Simultaneously Britain involved itself in covert, opaque deals to line its coffers indirectly through a state-sponsored offshore mining multinational working in the African nation. Because our government tends to sleepwalk over making quick decisions we catch up by 'fudge 'n' nudge' other means, i.e.: economic warfare or political subversion in plausible deniability mode…while, concurrently, preserving its reputation for fair play and decency in international affairs. Such is the secret way we do things in Britain – and we do it well. The antonym is of a vulture feeding on a carcass. Over the years I have come to recognise that the British populace are one of the most lied to of all, via the controlled mainstream media.

All I do know is Gonzalo, if indeed that was his real name (like mine wasn't), wasn't wrong in his surmising about Angola's near future and like a knobhead I nearly screwed it up by almost divulging the fact I was an intelligence officer. (For non-Brits it's a vulgar slang for a stupid person.) In my defence, the short trip was my first ever job by myself for SIS abroad and I haven't ever repeated my near mistake.

I have also got a lot wiser since then, especially investigating what lies behind the conflicting explanations given by various witnesses. *I expect the unexpected.* Nietzsche's dictum truly applies, especially when applied to espionage situations, *'there are no facts, only interpretations'*, because observers see events from different angles and core beliefs, and then our reports from the field are wilfully altered behind closed doors to fit a pre-ordained end result. *I fear for what the public doesn't know that lies ahead.*

I discovered it can be quite lonely out there on your own surrounded by millions. But being alone didn't turn me inwards – rather it expanded my horizons to better understand my surroundings. The deeper in I went, the complexities and contradictions became never-endingly denser. Like playing a silent game of chess with the flawed human emotions of strangers – where anything can happen, and sometimes suddenly does. *Equally, it's a solitary life knowing national secrets that I didn't necessarily agree with.* Nevertheless, I found out from the exercise in Portugal I've one got of those mentalities that keeps ticking over, even when I sleep. By living in the moment, you learn from such madcap experiences, trying to remain clear-thinking and recognising the realities, dissecting and reflecting, while focusing on the rapidly multiplying lines that are getting murkier by the minute. The 'combined and uneven developments', as it were.

I was quite chuffed when my line manager later on noted "that most people appear to be looking for something they haven't seen before", but concluded I possessed "a kind of 'oneoffness' and that I processed information and memorised differently to the norm". But what is normal?

I'm still trying to find out! *I do think those of us who have seen action for our country in areas of conflict, moves us into a different space than others who haven't experienced it.*

When you keep progressing onwards, you win.
When you don't move forward, you lose.
Failure is when you give up.
You deserve luck when you are positive.
It's a state of mind to be the open-thinking kind.

And I still sport that scar on my elbow from the camel who had the hump!

* * * * * * *

Chapter Two

The end of the sixties and the beginning of the seventies saw an extraordinary and unexpected surge in demand for Western-based pop music in Soviet-controlled countries.

Bootlegging and illegally imported vinyl records took off, to satisfy the huge hunger for new music by fans living behind the Iron Curtain. For many years, if not decades, people of all ages in Eastern Europe had been listening to foreign radio stations for their regular batch of unfiltered news from the West. Chief among the far-reaching shortwave stations was the venerable London-based British Broadcasting Corporation, better known as the BBC. The broadcasts by Auntie Beeb, as Brits affectionately called it, were on several channels but BBC *Radio1* was the main airwave modern Britpop was played on. The other notable newscasters were *Voice of America* (headquartered in Washington, DC) and *Radio Free Europe/Radio Liberty* then based in Munich, West Germany. Both were owned and funded by the US government. Though their charter was supposedly 'to broadcast accurate, balanced, and comprehensive news and information to an international audience', they were largely engaged in disseminating American-style propaganda to communist countries. But they also played some music, and the many youth on the other side of the Iron Curtain tuned in to listen. Such a pastime, however, was deemed by the Soviet bloc governments as decadent and anti-social.

The reality was that the local authorities could do nothing to prevent the younger masses from spending money on such trivial pursuits. Those in charge in the eastern territories continued to believe that, if left unchecked, the 'western sounds would eventually warp the mind-set of future generations'. And yet they were powerless to effectively fight this trend, short of enacting draconian measures that would bring back the terrors of the Stalinist regime.

To thwart this perceived threat that was 'corrupting' the minds of the masses in the eastern bloc, the military authorities regularly engaged in the blocking of the electronic transmissions originating in the West. Ironically, conscripts of the red military who were tasked with jamming activities, spent their own down time around the radio singing along and jammin' of a different kind to the hit melodies featured on the playlists. The majority of these kids didn't know what the lyrics to the songs were about nor what the English words meant. But to them, the contemporary sounds represented an inspired change for the better from the endless classical music and opera normally heard on the local, regime-owned radio stations. And then in 1956, the Poles ignored their masters in Moscow and stopped the blockade of foreign frequencies altogether. Unable to prevent this move from the old to the new the Russians claimed, at first, that they 'permitted a democratisation process for their free-thinking neighbours'. *But later on, the Soviets saw matters on an entirely different wavelength and, in due course, acted upon the opportunity to achieve other means that were more important to them.*

The uneasy and unofficial laissez-faire arrangement came to a head when several smugglers (mainly from West Germany and Sweden) were apprehended at various border control points along the line where west meets east. The solo drivers, fuelled by entrepreneurial spirit, took to the road in the hope of making quick money. They loaded their car boots (trunks) with albums by western artists and intended to sell them for hard currency only. They were illicitly attempting to meet demand. Had thousands, if not millions, of bank notes in US dollars, British pounds sterling, West German deutschmarks and Swiss francs left the country in their hands, it would have severely drained the cash reserves held in the coffers of the Marxist states. The ruling classes needed the money to remain in-country to pay for more productive tools such as tractors, construction cranes and other equipment needed to support the agricultural and manufacturing collectives nationwide.

At the time, The World Bank, International Monetary Fund and wealthy attendees of the then two-year old European Management Forum (later renamed the World Economic Forum) were the primary sources of international funding. In keeping with their capitalist intent of undermining socialism, these bodies insisted that the Soviet Union and its sphere of influence in Albania, Bulgaria, Czechoslovakia, East Germany, Hungary, Poland, Romania and Yugoslavia, pay for all their purchased imports in hard currency. And so, the eastern bloc countries were forced to pay for the purchases in western denominations. Naturally, recorded music from the west was not considered of vital importance to the well-being of the citizens or the development of the states allied with the Soviet Union. But western recorded music gradually became a powerful tool for Eastern Europe to counter the western political programmes in place.

* * * * * * * * *

One day early in 1974, the British government received an official enquiry from the Polish People's Republic through its Ministry of Industry and Commerce (*Ministerstwo Przemysłu i Handlu*). The formal request by the government of Poland invited the British authorities to tender a proposal for the legal importation of vinyl records to Poland. This seemingly progressive concept was intended to regulate the illegal traffic of recorded music and to counter the illicit trade of albums sold at inflated prices to the 'corrupted children of the revolution'. The Polish government was eager to stem the loss of western cash via the black-market back channels, while simultaneously benefiting from the mark-up on the street. Poland had a long history of passively resisting totalitarian dictatorship and considered this approach as the best way to transform their society into the system of their own choosing. In a sense, this narrative is about how that restraint was slowly loosened from the iron grip of Mother Russia and how the motherland turned that loss of control into a perceived advantage.

The catalysts for this unusual initiative undertaken by Poland were none other than The Beatles. The distinctive compositions, mostly by Lennon & McCartney, had catapulted the group to global fame and brought them into the homes of millions of young people. Their success resulted in worldwide sales in the hundreds of millions and contributed towards making recorded and printed music the UK's third largest export at the time. In Poland, young men and indeed many girls began sporting hairstyles like the Liverpudlian icons. Not surprisingly, young girls also started to copy the fashion of the high-profile women in the lives of the famous group by sporting mini-skirts, despite widespread disdain and even outright condemnation from their elders. The phenomenal increase in sales of recorded music was to follow down the same path. The London-based Polish government In-exile was all too happy and made sure that the demand for vinyl records undermined their collectivist rivals in the homeland.

In the heyday of this musical revolution, the record label of the famous British foursome was The Gramophone Company through its Parlophone subsidiary. But by 1973 the imprint was reorganised and became known as EMI Records (an acronym for Electrical and Musical Industries). For more than 40 years EMI's non-music side had been built upon a strong background in radar development and manufacture of defence equipment. Its relationship with all of Britain's security agencies was well-known to those who worked at the Secret Intelligence Service, the international part of the country's spy apparatus. The multinational corporation had long cooperated with the British government on national security issues by providing operational cover for the SIS when occasionally asked to do so. Many other British firms had similarly participated in such activities over the prior decades.

It wasn't long after receiving this unusual request, that the SIS selected a junior intelligence officer to accompany a duo from EMI's international division to hold preliminary talks with Polish government officials in Warsaw. The two EMI executives were to explore possible parameters for the unusual proposed venture and to determine if such cooperation could bear fruit for both sides of the divide. The SIS man was in the team for non-music reasons.

* * * * * * * * *

As a prelude to our upcoming trip, I met my counterparts at EMI's record manufacturing plant in Hayes, a small town situated just southwest of the capital and a stone's throw from the main runways of London Heathrow Airport. To me, neither man looked a natural fit to the music industry. Rather, they were bespectacled Burberry-attired suit 'n' tie business administrators who drank a lot of tea. They appeared to be in their mid-40s, presumably married with children, with mortgages to pay and short back and sides' type haircuts. In contrast, I was a single man with no commitment whatsoever. I wore smart but casual clothes then seen in fashionable Carnaby Street. Admittedly, I didn't have a Beatles hairstyle, with my raffish five o'clock shadow completing the typical sketch of an arty person being more along the lines of the Rolling Stones.

One of the executives was the company's export manager while the other was its licensing expert. Both Englishmen were fluent in French and German. EMI's main creative centre was in London at Manchester Square, W1. Apparently, there wasn't much liaison between the two UK company offices. EMI was after all, a truly multinational corporation that maintained bureaus in practically all corners of the world. The pair who will remain nameless, were told I had only just joined the organisation, in the newly-formed 'development section' housed in a non-descript office building around the corner from headquarters in Marylebone High Street. In truth, it was nothing more than one sparsely furnished room that had a gold metal EMI nameplate tacked on its door. It was staffed full-time by a young cockney lady going by the name of Flora, who showed up 9-5, Monday to Friday and answered the phone. Two burly doormen, stationed downstairs in the foyer, took care of the building's security during office hours. The firm's name also appeared on the office index in the lobby, along with dozens of other companies renting space in the building, but none were connected to EMI.

The truth is there was only one EMI employee in the UK who spoke fluent Polish. She was a young, recently married woman who worked in the royalties department as a mid-level office manager. The human resources department of EMI reported that there was nobody else among the hundreds of EMI employees in Britain who understood any Eastern European language to any great degree. So, SIS chose the next best thing they had: a fledging intelligence officer fluent in Russian who also knew how the music trade worked to a reasonable extent. This knowledge dated back to his college years in northern England where he sat on the entertainment committee and was in charge of selecting, booking and organising recording artists to perform at live gigs.

I met the other two fellows every day during normal business hours for a week prior to our departure. I am pretty sure I initially attracted some derision from them due to my dress code and youngish looks. I think my overall knowledge of the business won them over in due course and erased any negative preconceived notions they may have had of me, and on a number of opinions I held. In fact, I followed musical trends and various genres far more than they ever did. Towards the end of our initiation time together I could see how 'development' would encompass a vast array of related subject matters. I also got to understand export and licensing better. We each respected our individual know-how. But all-night ravers they were not!

We then had the weekend off. At the crack of dawn on the following Monday, we flew on a narrow-bodied brand-new LOT Polish Airlines' Soviet-made Ilyushin IL-62 jet to Warsaw. Interestingly the word *lotnicze*, which is abbreviated to 'lot', means flights in Polish. I hadn't been this far to the east since I had been a university student in Moscow four years previously and I admit lapsing into memory lane. In my head I was listening to the Beatles' song "Back in the USSR". Though it was the beginning of summer, coming down through the clouds for landing, I could only see whiteness everywhere. It felt like I was spinning back in time to the snow-covered steppes of Russia and I momentarily heard balalaikas strumming. *I subconsciously took this certain familiarity as a message from the gods as starting from a blank page on this operation, basically playing everything by ear.* In the history of recorded music and espionage nothing like this had ever transpired before. As the aircraft, which resembled a replica of a British-made Vickers VC10, turned for its final approach, the sounds I heard faded away when the sun's glare segued into the vast expanses of bright green and brown surrounding Warsaw.

We were greeted in the arrival hall by a stoic bulky lad holding the sign EMI. He silently drove us from the airport into downtown Warsaw in a Soviet-made four-seat Zhiguli, which is the same as a Lada, (basically a large Polski Fiat), to the Grand Hotel. People were walking around in short sleeves and summer dresses. The girls were generally very pretty, ready to smile at strangers staring at them. I was all too happy to reciprocate.

We ate a rather tasteless lunch and washed it down with mud-like Turkish coffee. We then trudged 15 minutes over to the designated meeting place. All along, my two companions were more interested in looking in shop windows for items to buy for their wives and children. Through the reflection of the glass I couldn't help but notice the square-built minder that was keeping an eye on us some 50 paces behind. He moved when we moved, stopped when we stopped, so I couldn't miss him. Like the car driver earlier, there was 'an informed pattern' about them, *uzor* in Russian, in how they presented themselves to my practised eye.

Before long we were sitting in a no-frills meeting room on the third floor of the Polish Ministry of Industry & Commerce. Facing us across the table were three of its managers. Two of them were uncomfortably stiff men in their 40s. They smiled thinly and nodded a lot. The third was a stern looking older girl who assumed the role of the interpreter. I found myself observing a prominent angry vein on her neck that suggested to me she didn't want to grace our presence. And indeed, the old dragon with the hard plastic face did all she could to prove her point. She was rather curt and acted with old school vindictiveness at all times towards us. She absolutely refused to establish eye contact with me, that part was certain, perhaps because I was the most junior member at the table. In the past, this sort of body language usually made me smile inwardly, as I never took the intended slight personally. For the most part, I tended to assume the mind-set of 'well, let's see what this is all about then, unlocking things the communist way. The start of the *Magical Mystery Tour*, sic'.

Our hosts were in no hurry to get into substantive matters, it seemed. Turned out this was only the getting to know your ugly mug introductory phase. We began the session with the mutual trading of business cards, mine included – with the title of 'development representative' embossed on it – which she rubbed repeatedly, slowly with her thumb, as if there was some kind of sexual gratification in the act.

We then all took turns at naming the languages we each understood. I elected to play the role of the village idiot, probably because I was the youngest present. For reasons I didn't want to express, I spluttered that I only spoke English, failing to bring up my fluency of Russian. My British colleagues, much to their credit, didn't flinch. Had they glanced over at me or squeaked uncomfortably in their seats, they would have given the game away. From this introductory session we learned that the main meeting would be held first thing the next morning with higher ups in attendance. Even during the late exchanges, the hoary bag continued to expose her mean streak for all to see. She once directed an unnecessary taunt at my fellow associates by questioning their understanding of German with, "What is the Teutonic word for: a project rushed to produce early results at a cost to its quality?"

Nobody had a clue but I muttered the answer in Russian to myself, *'Shturmovschina.'*

Instead I chose to ask her why? Eyes still averted, her response was very insightful and consistent with her odd behaviour, "Because of this, what we are doing here. I am thinking your trip to Poland is wasted because we have not yet the answer on how to do this transaction properly."

"Where's there's a will then we will find a way," replied the EMI export manager brightly, before getting up to leave, effectively ending further strained dialogue.

Along the corridor on the way out I overheard her behind me say in Russian to one of the blokes I thought was Polish, "The English are so full of themselves." I grinned widely to myself without her seeing me do so.

So back we trooped to the box-like hotel rooms at the Grand to change out of our business clothes before heading for a few hours walkabout in the city centre. Later in the evening, we Brits all had an unremarkable dinner together in the next-door Russian restaurant. From our few hours of sightseeing, the Politburo's policies clearly dominated a lot of Polish life. So the topic of conversation at the table, I remember well, turned to the validity of a quotation attributed to Nikita Khruschev, the Soviet Union leader. He had reportedly once famously exclaimed, *"As God is my witness, we have no spies."* I had argued with my compatriots that he was actually telling the truth in his own way. I explained that the communists didn't believe in any gods, and spies in the eastern bloc were described internally as scouts. My 'translation of English into another English' made my two companions chuckle.

After our meal together, we had each turned in early for the night. It all made for a hard day's night. The door squeaked like a mouse and had half an inch space at the bottom. The walls were so thin I could hear every move by whomever, not only to the left and right of me but also from above and below. The hotel's dilapidated water system pumped like a combustion engine. The shower was cold, with weak pressure. There was no functioning air conditioning either, so I was forced to leave the window ajar. Unfortunately, the added noise from the traffic below kept me awake for a good part of the warm evening. All in all, it was not a good start to my first time in *Polska*, as Poland calls itself. But in the words of Leo Tolstoy, *'If you want to be happy, be.'* So I finally fell asleep.

I woke up late, fell out bed and dragged a comb across my head. Then made my way downstairs. We were back again at the Ministry after breakfast. I looked *forward* to seeing the rude battle axe again, such is my personality. Interestingly the same security detail followed us again. No effort to change his appearance or style. My associates were completely oblivious to him, still. I didn't bother mentioning his presence to them either. Such a happy jovial fellow he wasn't. He was with us, too, when we did our touristy thing the previous afternoon.

The new group at the meeting numbered half a dozen. More energy abounded. They were clearly high-level bosses, except for one of them. The two fellows from yesterday had apparently outlived their usefulness and had been duly discharged from any additional duty. The gruff elderly woman, however, remained as the translator, sitting in the same high chair as before, wearing an identical outer garment as the day before. One other man now also spoke English. His name was Marek and I got to get pally with him over the next few months. He and I were the only ones not wearing a suit and tie. Both of us clearly the youngest by 20 years to everybody else. In a sense he was the Polish version of me, which balanced out the coming proceedings nicely as far as I was concerned. But you couldn't help but notice that the seven of them were sitting directly across the oblong table from our trio. I wondered why they had not made an effort to interact better with us by setting the discussion around a nearby round table that was available for use. It presented an 'us and them' scenario. But later I got to thinking that the accepted ways of capitalism weren't a part of their thinking. They weren't bad people, except for the woman interpreting. Even later again I figured wherever the miniature cameras were placed, we were facing them.

After the usual exchange of business cards, we got down to work. We were presented with a typed list of British recording artists, as the sourpuss lady put it, "acceptable for Polish ears". The names there represented a variety of musical genres, from popular through folk to heavy metal. The list included The Beatles, The Rolling Stones, Tyrannosaurus Rex, Lindisfarne, Kate Bush, Sheena Easton, David Bowie, Rod Stewart, Roxy Music, Deep Purple and Iron Maiden.

I quickly pointed out to them that David Bowie was not an act signed to EMI as yet. Marek responded affably with, "Ah, yes, sorry, he is with RCA, Record Company of America, no?"

"Radio Corporation of America," I corrected him. We smiled with our eyes across the divide. The old girl just stared at us as if we were some kind of contaminating vermin without bothering to tell the others. I got a strong sense then that she probably thought we two longer-haired boys were secretly faggots. He might have been but I certainly wasn't.

My colleagues then began pitching the repertoire by Elton John, Hot Chocolate and Gary Glitter. They were cut-off as soon as they began their pitch. Our Polish hosts deemed them "unsuitable". Needless to say, we were flummoxed as to why these artists were not acceptable, while others were. We tried to go deeper but they refused to engage us on the subject. The most they were willing to say was that "their backgrounds had been investigated thoroughly". It left us scratching our heads.

We moved on. One of my British teammates next coughed up, "Once we have determined the amount ordered, I am instructed to ask how the Polish government intends to pay us? We are flexible should you choose a denomination other than pounds sterling."

We scanned the faces in front of us while the old dear asked the question of them in their own lingo. Some shifted uncomfortably on their bums during the process, while others scratched their necks. As we waited patiently, the dialogue grunted to and fro between them for several minutes with much nodding and nays.

…it was about then I realised that whatever we said to them was translated faster than what they said to us. I reasoned that this time delay was probably so somebody unseen in an adjoining room could halt any mention of Polish government classified information being transmitted…

The answer eventually came. "We would like to barter you with anything you would like, to the equal value of, from our glorious Polish-made products."

It was now our turn to look dumbfounded. We Brits glanced at each other. I could see the pair were already going into reject mode. Wearing my SIS cap, I suddenly detected an opportunity. I turned away from them to relate the inspiration to the committee. "Can you please furnish a list of what you have in mind?"

"Yes, we can have this for you tomorrow."

"We would need to inspect the factories to assure ourselves that the products are of good quality, of course. I'm sure you understand this requirement must be met first and foremost."

Another long-ish conversation among the Polish ensued. At the end of the tête-a-tête, the white witch announced rather grandly, "*All* of our manufacturing is world-class. But it is impossible to show you everything we make, to have samples sent here, you must understand…"

I shrugged and continued, "Then the only way this transaction can happen is if you provide nationwide clearance with the various authorities so a representative can travel without restriction to see for himself on our behalf."

It was the first time she actually looked at me. Well, she positively looked *into* me at length then, not with any newly-gained respect but in total bewilderment. Gazing at her slightly gawping mouth I silently declared victory to myself, clenching my fist under the table as if I'd scored a winning goal. My first brownie points in the bag!

She spoke to me hesitantly without referring to the esteemed panel decked out in polyester suits, bar Marek, on her right, "Yes, I'm sure that can be arranged. Who would that person be? We would need a name so he can clear police and army checks in the industrial areas in mind. And for what duration would the permit be needed?"

I could feel the twin glare of British eyes boring holes into me as I spoke. "I propose myself and I would need two calendar months carte blanche to fully carry out this intrusive imposition on you. But the inspection is required by our country before we can execute a formal business agreement. It would have to be done before your winter arrives, which will then make such an assessment impossible until the following spring. In the meantime, the longer you delay, I'm afraid, more precious money will be draining from Poland through the back door."

Following a slight pause two heads of the men opposite us moved forward in slight acknowledgement, indicating they knew my language better than they had previously let on. Funny really as both blinked rapidly at all times indicating to me they were overly thinking or living a lie. It turned out to be the latter.

It was an Englishman's hollow voice that made me turn to look at him. "Yes, well, all this is fine and dandy but it is beyond where our red lines are drawn. We must return home tomorrow as we are busy with making actual profits for export. We can spend the rest of today helping our Polish compatriots compile a list of music titles you desire and the corresponding quantities you may need. But our esteemed colleague is on his own regarding what he is proposing to you."

So that's how matters were generally concluded at the time. The pre-order on paper surprisingly came to just over a million pounds sterling. A lot of dough in 1974. The EMI lads were gobsmacked at the total but the question of how payment would be made still had to be worked out.

When we got home to our little island, some bosses at the SIS seemed content with the arrangements – the most senior none other than the Controller for Eastern Europe – while I had my knuckles rapped by others for my chutzpah. I was told I was also responsible for the selling-on of whatever items I selected for swap. And, naturally, while I was gallivanting around Poland, I would serve another purpose by discreetly checking out military installations and undertake other defence-related ops.

The long and short of the episode is that a month later I was back by myself in Poland. The Polish government allocated me a Polski Fiat car. Not surprisingly, it was bugged. But the Warsaw-based SIS officer showed me how to 'accidentally' disable the device, if and when needed, by simply hanging my overcoat over it. The vehicle fortunately did not have a tracker on it, despite secret and exhaustive tests performed by the British techies based in Poland to find one. This latter task was carried out at night in a semi-covered car park before I set off the next morning. I was, of course informed in advance where to park it. I gathered that the Poles did not tag (surveillance) me. They probably expected that I would be stopped at random road checks by armed forces and the police as I made my way around the countryside with a Polish government signed letter allowing me all-access. And they would report back that I'd swung by. 'Mrs Miserable-ski' and her team in Warsaw would be arranging the appointments with whomever I wanted to see, as well as organising my hotel reservations. So I was properly supervised to an extent.

* * * * * * * * *

One needs to comprehend the face of the object
before one proceeds to conquer it.

So off I went to the adventurous horizon, another day in the life of me. A 23-year old British SIS intelligence officer given the freedom to roam in enemy territory, courtesy of the adversary, to glean information that ultimately may be used against them. I nicknamed it My Three Grand Holiday as I was given £3,000 spending money and ended up staying in three hotels named the Grand three stops in a row. Plus there were three times I faced threats that made me sweat.

For eight weeks I chose to motor my way around the country in a counter-clockwise pattern. Starting from Warsaw, I headed to Poznań, Szczecin, Gdańsk, nearby Sopot, Toruń, Warsaw again, Kraków, Katowice, Wrocław and Łódź (pronounced Woots). I ended up back in the Polish capital a second time at the halfway stage. Warsaw is known as *Warszawa* in Polish, as the road signs indicated frequently. Under SIS orders, I had shortened my hair to appear 'less homosexual' in Polish conservative eyes.

Everything from footwear to gingerbread and from porcelain to vodka production was inspected under this very gracious bending of the rigid rules. Many factory managers and *robotniks* (workers) looked at me as a bit of novelty but were generally amenable to showing me around their plants and furnishing the inner-workings details on their products. Still, adopting hiding in plain sight methods, I managed to work into my itinerary half a dozen unscheduled stops as well. I met one agent, as instructed to by SIS before departing London. I also collected a couple of dead drops as ordered to by my superiors before I left the UK. I visited the periphery of three strategic installations and scouted militarised zones.

In one specific assignment, I confirmed that a previously unknown armament factory existed in a dense forest. In order to pull off the job without being detected, I wore some second-hand overalls I had bought at an outdoor market earlier. I left my usually-worn clothes in the car and took two buses to and from the area, trudging several miles in the woods and trying not to stand on dried twigs as the snap reminded me of shots being fired.

Once inside the darkness of the denser trees it was bleak and damp as no sun's rays penetrated, and I temporarily lost my direction despite utilising my secret button-size compass (removed from my jacket left in the car over the bug). Then I spotted a large tusked boar in the distance, making his way like I was. Actually, it was his steaming smoky breath that caught my eye, mistakenly thinking it was a sentry hiding there having a cigarette. We both halted in our tracks, fleetingly, to stare at each other and then continued down our respective paths. *In the loneliness of these hours strangely I felt I had a lot in common with that muscular wild beast, as we were both foraging for different reasons.* It was an extraordinary experience, too, because the birdsong had stopped in unison when we had stood eyeing each other up. But it wasn't anything to do with us because out of the silence, seconds later, an army helicopter roared loudly over the top, coming down in the near distance. Its rotors thankfully redirected me to where I needed to go. At that split instance I had momentarily slammed myself to the floor in fright. My most dangerous moment thus far during the op.

Just before leaving London, I had been instructed to clandestinely meet a certain chap I knew next to nothing about. The RVP (rendezvous point) had been scheduled in advance. I was to connect with the contact at 3 AM at a house address I'd committed to memory. It was only a ten-minute walking distance from the old family-run hotel I was staying at for the night. The walk through dark-lit alleys and shadows freaked me out, and led me to believe I was in for an eerie encounter. It was a creepy time indeed, probably the second most surreptitious half an hour of the entire two-month trip. I must admit I had goose-bumps and was swearing under my breath.

F-f-fear kept me focused while formulating fixes to this frigging foolishness.

Not really knowing what to expect, I prepared for my upcoming ordeal by fully applying my arsenal of tradecraft, gripping my miniature one bullet pen gun, all along dripping in emotional cold panic. After slowly mounting a creaky staircase and entering an unlocked room at the top, under the faint light of a candle I could see an elderly, bearded Russian priest, standing there rigidly. Thin, tall and taciturn, he reminded me of a mysterious grey-haired Rasputin. We whispered statically in his language for ten minutes as he asked me how my factory visits were coming along. At the close, he handed me a small wooden varnished vial "for delivery to London". When rattled, it clearly had no liquid in it. By way of explanation, the pastoral man said he represented *Svyashchennyy Soyuz*, which took me a while to decipher in my head. Translated, it is The Holy Alliance. I was thinking back to the fact the Russian and Italian mob work together on big projects… When you are 23 and following orders, it is not your place to ask questions. You only do as you are told, which I diligently carried out to the letter. He obviously knew what I was doing in Poland and who I represented. I have since investigated what THA are about. As a confirmed atheist, I am not in favour of supporting any endeavours promoted by an illuminati-level secret society with shady political-financial interests in the name of God – based behind the Iron Curtain or not. This kind of work evidently throws together unlikely bedfellows. I was surprised the SIS continued being associated with these kinds of organisations. Perhaps the answer lies in SIS' charter (known as the Order Book), which defines or mandates its function.

The most interesting and personally satisfying experience occurred at the state-owned vodka distilleries' *Polski Monopol Spirytusowy* (Polish Spirits Monopoly), which was shortened to Polmos. (In Russian *voda* means water but in Polish it was spelt *woda*, which translated as little water). I visited several locations. They were all well-run plants. I can also confirm that Poland does indeed manufacture the *best vodka in the world*, especially the product made from locally-grown rye. I should add that while I have never been drunk in my life, I did tipple for taste on each occasion, and why not!

Midway through my countrywide trip, I gave myself a well-deserved break. Pretending to be a Russian tourist, I took a brief detour to Sopot. This Polish beach resort is on the outskirts of Gdańsk, once known as Danzig – its original German name. There, I got the sense that the locals didn't see themselves as really being part of Poland. German was clearly the prevalent language in this region. My proficiency of Russian was of no help at all, as the few people I approached defiantly refused to engage me in conversation. And I got plenty of quizzical looks with my pitiful attempts at Polish. But I took this snub in my stride as I reminded myself that the French do this to the British, Americans and anyone else who is insolent enough to converse in English on French soil. I cannot explain to this day why I stupidly lapsed into Russian. It certainly was a mistake to allow the devil may care to kick in. But it was the only time I spoke Russian (for a few hours) on the whole trip, apart from the earlier ten-minute conversation with the Rasputin-like character.

The more I thought about that charmless man I realised he wasn't a fully-rounded personality and sported an element of being damaged – perhaps had a chip on his shoulder. He presented the old way of doing things. His persona made me shudder and as a result I focused more on the job at hand.

Sopot was once the most fashionable pre-war resort on the Baltic Sea. Despite the passage of time, the place, or what was left of it, still exuded an underlying atmospheric feel of 19th-century elegance. Communist beach babes paraded in western bikinis with eastern mind sets. I stayed for four nights in a basic room with a sea view at the Grand Hotel, a throwback to a previous century. Not too far away is Hel, a thin strip of land with wind-deformed pine trees. It certainly wasn't a heavenly paradise. Nearby is also Leba, the Polish Sahara Desert. High sand dunes surrealistically, in slow motion, are spreading inland destroying everything in their path. I couldn't say I enjoyed myself there as the whole area was of strangeness and churlish geographical disfigurements – a dreamlike anti-beauty. *As I stood at the open hotel window nightly, I had an eerie understanding of how it was for a free man overlooking this quasi-syndicalist and bohemian world with so much history. A place you must use, or it will absorb you, because if you gaze too long across the landscape, the landscape also gazes across you, just like communism does.*

After Sopot, I stopped for a one-night stay in Toruń, also at a hotel named the Grand. Then I ended up staying at the Grand Hotel again in Warsaw for two nights.

Once back in the Polish capital, I got the expected message from the British embassy. The discreet brush-pass of receiving information was done by prior arrangement with a fellow from the British embassy. The main gist of the message was that my car could have now had a tracking device placed on the chassis. It was something I had already assumed had taken place since I had parked it outside on the street the whole time I'd been on the road.

Afterwards, I felt like letting my hair down for once, to escape this existence. On that first evening, the hotel was full of partying university students. As a matter of fact, the Communist Party Association of Polish Students was headquartered around the corner on Ulica Ordynacka. At the bar, I met a ravishing black-haired Polish girl called Mariska who thought I closely resembled Paul McCartney. We spent an exhaustive, enjoyable and animalistic evening in each other's company. Did I think she was a plant? Yes, I initially did, but in the end, I figured she wasn't. During the course of the evening, she disclosed in heavily-accented English that she was an anonymous editor for the Polish dissident periodical *Zeszyty Literackie*. At the time, the paper was in underground circulation. In English I gather it loosely means literature exercise books. Little did she know who I really was, and never will. To her I was just a British businessman visiting her country, a few years older than her, who happened to look like a Beatle.

I eventually read the English translation of her article back in London. In it anger boiled on the page, a jigsaw of words spewing forth hot spittle, much like the way she made love. I had kept the copy she had given me and took it back home for my real employer's political section to look over. I was later informed that, for the first time, SIS got an inkling that Poland was ready to revolt against their Soviet masters. Yet, contradictorily, I was never told what I had transported back home as a trinket from the creepy priest, but I managed to reasonably connect the dots from what transpired later. It was the eventual bank transfer process that triggered my thinking.

There must be a passion for preventing the people's thinking
that allows one human to objectify another.
This was the basic premise why communism
wasn't going to work.

* * * * * * * * *

On the second day of my stay in Warsaw, I hosted Marek for an extended lunch. Just after our repast, while walking back to my hotel, Marek brazenly and suddenly disclosed to me that he was an intelligence officer for

Służba Bezpieczeństwa Ministerstwa Spraw Wewnętrznych (Security Service of the Ministry of Internal Affairs). "The SB, I'm sure you have heard of us. I am assigned to escort you for the rest of your visit around Poland." I was not in a position to decline.

I don't know if he knew I was with SIS or not, but I played the dumb EMI man nonetheless. I endured a few moments of sheer panic thinking about whether the SB had picked up the trail of Mr Rasputin. No less worrisome was whether I had been unmasked for my recklessness by dropping into Russian in Sopot for a couple of hours. I wondered, too, why he had later on suggested an exfiltration to Britain. "One day I want to defect to your country. Surely you can open some doors for me when you get home?" he had whispered. "Perhaps we can discuss this more in the car in the weeks to come." I didn't say anything about the bug that had probably been planted in the Polski Fiat by his group. I did realistically gather that I also had a human tracker to deal with now. I remained mum on the topic and he never managed to suck me into a conversation for the rest of my time in Poland, despite his attempts to repeatedly engage me on his possible defection.

Unlike me, Marek had decidedly effeminate features and gestures. We often had to share a room simply due to lack of availability. He never had to shave regularly like me. And he would stare at my torso whenever I was topless, his nostrils flared, which betrayed his sexual orientation. *I counted these odd moments my third most perilous in Poland.* I didn't want to attract male rape. I never took my eyes off what I was drinking when he was around as he could easily drop in a drug, especially in the evenings when we were sucking down beer together.

Once, during those three weeks together, the genial Marek mentioned to me that the particular region we were travelling through was famous for *fresh* duck. Was I hungry to eat some? So, we stopped in a roadside inn, ordered a plate each from the innkeeper and drank some ale to await the food. After 45 minutes and feeling peckish, I asked why it was taking such a long time for the meal to come to the table. With a straight face, Marek responded, "Remember that loud bang we heard half an hour ago?" Yes indeed, there was a shot fired in the distance that made us stop talking for a moment. "Well, the cook got the bird as it flew past."

I thought that a very funny quip at the time. Turned out he wasn't telling a joke. Our cultural differences and ways of understanding didn't allow him to get my return wise-crack either. I'd responded poker-faced, "So it wasn't a fowl-up then." He just sat there looking blank at me.

The steaming plates came eventually and I recall us removing buckshot from the flesh. It was probably the freshest meat I'd ever tasted. But the experience contributed to me becoming mostly a pescatarian (seafood eater) from that moment on. Since then I have continued to avoid dark meats. I couldn't help but know that meal I was eating was flying free as the wind less than an hour ago.

Being karmic and aware of circumstances around me, being immersed in this controlled world of communism, it reminded me of what it's like to have liberation removed forcibly, and that I'd have to be extra careful from here on, living inside a hot zone.

* * * * * * * * * *

I eventually settled this strangest of business deals by trading dried soup and canned ham in exchange for the vinyl records. It was way outside my remit. Nevertheless, I flew to Stockholm and dealt with the head buyer for a Swedish national supermarket. The company was willing to market the products under its own brand name. The Poles were only too happy to comply. Later on, that same retailing chain went for another order. This time around, the company ordered high-quality Polish vodka which it sold under its own private label.

With the business deal consummated, one mystery still remained. Who was the middle man, who had received the goods and sent them on to their intended destination? After all, much paperwork such as billing, fees, and insurance coverage were needed to effect the complex transactions across country borders. 'The Vatican Bank' was the one selected by sources unknown to me. It did so under its vague and misleading real name of *Instituto per le Opere di Religione* or Institute for Religious Works, better known in the banking fraternity as IOR.

I cannot swear on my life or on the gods to this, of course. I might even get hit with a bolt of lightning from the skies above. My encounter with the Rasputin lookalike crystallised my thoughts and led me to understand the unlikely transformation that had taken place in Poland. The country turned out over time to be probably the most pro-Catholic nation on earth and the powers that be who manipulate this belief managed to push the masses away from communism and towards capitalism. Nowadays, the republic imports music and pays for it in Euros. To this day I still prefer to drink Polish vodka. And their locally manufactured products are exported all over the world now. The hardworking Polish people have also taken over from the Irish as being the most exported (read as exploited) elsewhere. Somewhere along the line I would bet money that Marek, if that was his real name, left Poland of his own accord and now lives at an undetermined location in the west.

* * * * * * * * *

This story went an extra mile because during our time together Marek once asked me, uncharacteristically, to furnish him with some information about charities in Britain. He concluded his unusual query with "seeing as you are not a spy, perhaps this request can be met as a concerned citizen."

I did as he asked of me. I liked him as a person. He was no doubt gay but he must have realised from an early time that I was an alpha male. He had met Mariska briefly in the hotel restaurant just before she and I bid goodbye to each other. He never actually made any advances on me. At the same time, he never showed any interest in women during our road travels together, even though he had a chance to do so as we often also stayed in separate hotel rooms. Furthermore, I strictly stayed within my cover – knowing he worked for the SB. He said he was specifically interested in names of non-profit organisations that helped homosexuals and lesbians to come out. It opened my eyes wide as I was driving when I heard those words come out of his mouth. Eventually, I privately sent him the list he asked for to the purported home address he'd given me.

It appears 'come out' took on another composition, or maybe I heard it wrong to start with. It took me a while to learn about the macro plan executed by the Soviets through their Polish communist counterparts. One day, only a couple of years after this op concluded, I ran into my old-line officer/handler during that barter deal. While the SIS was and is a largely compartmented organisation, he felt sufficiently persuaded to fill me in with one of the strangest of events that materialised from that time.

Soon after the vinyl records started circulating around Poland, many ended up in other communist nations, especially copied later onto blank cassette tapes and illegally distributed to all and sundry. Around that time certain charities in Britain started to receive regular, large and anonymous contributions by bank transfer, all marked 'for the specific wellbeing of the third gender' – which indicated the funds came from the same source.

As the line officer explained, every year since, there had been a consistent number of asylum seekers turning up from Eastern Europe. The large majority of them openly homosexual, lesbian and transgender, with one-way tickets paid for by their governments. Each carried an identical note in their respective language with the names and addresses of the UK charitable foundations (when it was translated literally) 'who aided those with social exclusion and subversive sexual identity'.

"Based on pseudoscientific imagined values, their game plan was to ruin our country from the bottom up by exporting their undesirables to us, while removing a perceived stain on the fabric of their own countries," coughed the SIS lad.

I was initially puzzled about the moulding of this political agenda but later I read my SIS section's reports on a KGB man, one from the SB (not Marek) and a Stasi officer who had exfiltrated (defected), and provided further information on the increased unusual human flow west. The notes I made included the following:

As the Russian put it, "we long have deported to the west the physically disagreeable who spread depravity, disunity and discontent that undermined our national morale…it was a programme for the removal of the unacceptable".

The Pole explained it as "preventing further propaganda of non-traditional relationships that promoted an unwritten code of conduct among pure people". The rest of the man's interrogation more or less echoed Marek in terms of what the policy was that was put into motion by the SB – who thought the UK was soft.

The East German defector was on record as saying in his debriefing, "Queers are unacceptable as they encourage non-conformity in others with their improper behaviour. Buggery is unnatural, plain and simple. They are *Untermenschen* (sub-human) in their perverted thinking and lowly actions. Trying to subvert the general public with disgusting same sex motives should be classified as disabled or having a limited mental capacity. This degenerative shift happened in our society when we relaxed our defence of the values that underpin our cohesion, order and progress. So we had to cull these lesser people with reduced intellect the best we could. If we hadn't, then the next step would be people having anal intercourse with their pets with the conduct considered as normal. Perhaps even further down the line humans will be marrying animals or robots or objects of desire."

This intelligence was gleaned from classified files that still have not been cleared for declassification by sensitivity reviewers (normally stuffy, retired senior SIS officers) and remain in the archives long after their disclosure limit of 30 years minimum (though some can be held for a maximum of 60 years). Likely they have not yet passed through the weeding process, in which individual pages are removed and destroyed before reaching the deeper examination stage. Such is the controlled freedom of information in the UK. I admit I should not have made my notations and smuggled them out of the library. But I was intrigued that some foreign governments' policies were put into action on the back of our export programme, for a perceived greater good. I am also mindful that these turncoats still went ahead and came to the west despite their personal viewpoints on the pro and cons of both their respective eastern countries and ours. Our country obviously appealed to them more.

In later years when this outrageous plan became known to others, the official reason was explained that the Commies got the homophobic idea to expel gays from Fidel Castro in 1980. He had cleaned out the Cuban jails by letting the criminals duck out and 'escape' to the United States! Or it could be the other way around that Cuba got the précis years before from Poland. I have got wise to how the Communists publicly play these things by switching the onus. We do precisely the same as them.

* * * * * * * * *

Chapter Three

Almost three months had passed since I was transferred from Denmark to my new post in Switzerland. I reminded myself that I hadn't been to a warm climate for quite a while. Short trips on routine business matters to cold West Germany and frozen Austria did not help my mood. Truth be told, the area was just emerging from a frigid period of deep snow and icy winter. In fact, several avalanches had been reported in the nearby Alps.

On this particular overcast morning of early 1976, I was on the 10-minute tram ride from my new home to downtown Berne to SIS' secret station. I noted to myself that I hadn't driven my company car for quite some time. It had been stationary in my rented house's driveway for over two weeks.

We were three British SIS members of staff, and we presented ourselves as an international corporate travel agency. In the hierarchy, I was the number two, having been assigned the codename BEN/1. As matters stood, we were being overwhelmed by our own efforts to implement counter-measures against the world's largest Chinese collection of spies outside its capital of Beijing. Their embassy was right across the street from our office. Recently, we had discovered from our covertly placed monitoring devices that the Chinese had started to make definitive moves for an economic invasion of mainland Europe. The Chinese People's Liberation Army already had a full garrison outpost in Albania, and there was evidence that more troops were on the way to solidify and expand their base there. All these moves were carried out in plain daylight while Europeans slept peacefully and were oblivious to the dangers to their liberty.

Fortunately, SIS wasn't asleep. Five additional members of staff were scheduled to arrive soon in Berne to help us with the greatly expanded workload. But they hadn't arrived yet. Because we were struggling to cope, and Beijing had three dots in its name, we jokingly describing ourselves as '…the hot woks' (our own vernacular for working overtime)!

As I walked in the door, the head of station H/BEN, Barry Anderson (no relation), handed me my day's assignment. On top of the pile was a file that had just arrived by overnight pouch from London headquarters. "Do your best, by any means possible, mate, to find out more about this lot's worldwide objectives. Century House wants to know as a matter of urgency," he grunted. I was thinking then, yes, finally some travel overseas to a warmer climate will finally come my way!

I hung up my tweed overcoat and sat down at my desk with my cup of freshly brewed black coffee. Most ex-armed forces personnel drink it so because there's usually no milk, cream, half-and-half or sugar of any kind available out in the field. You eventually get used to sucking it down in its unadulterated, basic form and learn to enjoy the surge of caffeine without the adds-on.

I opened the envelope and pulled out a bunch of blown-up black and white A4 surveillance prints. They were all taken from afar. The first photo showed a group of elderly, white-haired or bald Caucasian men boarding a French-made Dassault private jet. An inscription on the back simply read: '7 July 1975, Madrid, Spain'. It was a mere nine months before I arrived to my new post in Berne and about 1,500 km (932 miles) away. In the back of my mind, I remember fancying the idea of visiting a warm place like Spain anytime soon!

The next picture made my eyes open wide. Taken at a cemetery, it showed a rather large assembly of people congregated at the site. The same group of old geezers were there standing to attention around a gravestone, *all performing the infamous Nazi salute!* Surrounding them, a group of young, light-skinned men stood sternly in identical poses. They were dressed in all-black attire and most of them were skinheads. A second ring of people drew my immediate attention and rather surprised me. They decidedly looked like Arab gentlemen. Some even wore traditional *kaffiyehs* (head-dresses). Interestingly enough, the inscription bore the same date as the previous picture. However, it had been taken in Vienna, Austria. Evidently, the assemblage (or at least some of them) had flown directly from Madrid to Vienna on the same day to pay their respects at the funeral of an unidentified dignitary of some prominence.

I next skimmed through a series of snaps taken face-on of older men with Germanic names. Stapled on the reverse of each photo, were passport shots of how these individuals looked as younger men. Most of them had held an officer rank of some sort. They had evidently served during World War II, in long defunct Nazi units. In the war-time pictures, many wore uniforms, but others didn't. Some of the younger white individuals were identified by name. One chap in particular, projected an aggressive appearance. He had a mini swastika tattooed on his forehead, Hindu-style. They were apparently all members of an openly active Nazi group identifying itself as Hilfskorp Arabien (Auxiliary Corps Arabia in German.) I'd never heard of it before. The sight of this gang made me squirm in discomfort. Interestingly, the packet did not contain any details or close-ups of those individuals of Arabic descent. The connection between the parties present at the cemetery was not explained and remained a mystery to me.

The next to last picture I looked at, was of an Austrian national. I'd definitely heard of him, but I had never seen his image before. He was identified as Otto Skorzeny. He had died in Madrid on 5 July 1975 and was cremated in his home town of Vienna. It explained the first two photographs I had just seen. I knew a bit about his background. He had been the recipient of numerous military awards for bravery and valour. Adolf Hitler himself had awarded him Germany's highest honour (my country's equivalent of the Victoria Cross.) His extensive war-time exploits and achievements were listed on the back. His military record was pretty impressive, I must say, despite the fact that he had been a member of the Nazi enemy. His nickname was Scarface. He did indeed carry a long, clearly visible weal on his left cheek from ear to mouth. As a younger man, he was wearing his black full-dress SS (Schutzstaffel meaning Protection Squadron – the Nazi Party's armed paramilitary wing) uniform. He appeared like a legendary bad boy film star in the frame. I stared at the officer's cruel appearance for ages. He had passed away at age 67, having lived a swashbuckling life of action. Some exploits attributed to him were no doubt fabricated for propaganda purposes but others were probably based on true events.

The last stand-alone shot I inspected was one of François Georges Albert Genoud, as he appeared in the present time. He was based in Lausanne, here in Switzerland, not far from where I was stationed. A little bit over an hour's drive away. I sighed to myself. Well, I thought, 'forget a trip abroad to a warm climate, at least the drive will get me out of the stifling office atmosphere for a while'.

I gazed intently at his semblance for a while, too. Born in Lausanne on 26 October 1915, which made him now 61. I pondered if I ever was going to gel with him in a face-to-face meeting. I was, after all, just 25. Seemingly, we had nothing in common.

I looked across the room at my two British compatriots talking on their phones. My boss, Barry was five years older than me while the other lad, Toby, BEN/2, was my age. He was, however, largely an administrator. So, the task fell on my lap. Perhaps I was selected because I had previously served as an officer in the Royal Navy's Fleet Air Arm.

Though a civilian, Genoud was said to be genuinely enamoured with anyone and everyone who wore a uniform. According to the accompanying report on him, he had met the Führer (Leader), Adolf Hitler, on numerous occasions. Genoud was believed to be the funder of the notorious ODESSA network. This secretive group organised and financed the escape of Nazi war criminals after the end of WWII. The ODESSA network cynically used the stolen assets of Jewish victims to help Nazi war criminals escape justice. He was also rumoured to be heavily involved in risky investments and/or money laundering operations. His funding activities routinely bordered on the shady side of business. Many of the toe-curling projects were in support of the European fascist underground. His growing affiliations with various Arab terrorist groups was equally disturbing. The man was a revolutionary through and through. He most clearly was a Nazi sympathiser, a virulent anti-Semite and an active sponsor of whoever the opposition was. He engaged in black market operations and was heavily involved in arms trafficking. All the while, he attempted to destabilise society norms by any means possible, especially if Jewish.

We were furnished with four addresses for Genoud. Two of them were in Lausanne while the other two were in the nearby villages of Villars-sur-Ollon and Pully, respectively. It seemed like he moved around. Probably for reasons that had to do with his own security. After the war ended, he had apparently lived in Tangier, Morocco, as well as in the Egyptian capital, Cairo.

Along with the four addresses, we were also given his still active post box in Lausanne. The subscription for *case postale 1315* had been paid upfront for the next two years. We could follow this trail in case we were unable to locate him at any of the four places. This titbit told me we had an informer inside the Swiss post office. If I ever needed the locality cased, I could probably depend on the insider. He or she would help me identify the individual who came to the main post office on a regular basis to extract the contents from the box. The main target was also known to frequent Lausanne's most upmarket hotel, the five-star Beau Rivage, several times a week. At least I had some options to go on.

The report disclosed that one of his closest associates was a private banker named Huber. His home address appeared to be within a short walking distance from my own residence in Berne. Fortunate coincidence, I thought! I immediately assumed the place was a detached house like mine. There was no available photo of how Huber looked. His first name wasn't known either. A part of the remit was to take some pictures of him and find out his Christian name.

To help me with my assignment, I enlisted the services of a neighbour's dog, a big Alsatian called Franco. I'd sometimes walked the friendly dog when my neighbour couldn't. It never occurred to me till that moment in time, that the dog carried the same name as the fascist dictator of Spain. I thought to myself, 'Well an oversized mutt with an extreme right-wing name was going to give me reasons to walk past Huber's place a few times…and we'd find some way to get the bloke's own name in full.' I could see now why my immediate boss, Barry, had selected me for the task at hand. I was, after all, a close neighbour of the secondary target.

Finding out more about Huber wasn't that hard, though it took a bit more time than I originally anticipated. Contrary to my preconceived notion, he did not live in a house. Rather, he lived in the only block of flats around there. The complex housed around 60 units. His apartment number hadn't been furnished. I had to find it.

The next morning, Franco and I did a nice job of filing in behind the busy bee postman. The Swiss can generally be depended on to work pretty much on schedule. As the letter carrier arrived to deliver the mail at the location in question, I was on full alert. I watched him insert the key in his possession to the locked glass double doors. From my vantage point, I observed him disappear down the stairs, presumably to the location of the post boxes. He emerged after a few minutes and left the building.

The day after, the hairy beast and I retraced our steps. We timed our routine to perfection. Just as the postman reappeared up the steps and came out, we met him at the door front. With utmost courtesy, he actually held the door open for us to allow us entry into the building. We exchanged *morgen* (morning) greetings. At the same time, the uniformed lad took an understandable wide berth of Franco. We skipped down to the basement and stood in front of the locked post boxes. They all had the apartment numbers prominently marked on them. All the mailman had to do to deliver the mail, was to insert the envelopes through the various open lids. With the tongs from my kitchen in my pocket, I could easily lift out anything that was in there, and read to whom the envelope was addressed. Many residents had their surnames printed neatly and conveniently on the front of the post box as well. That saved me the trouble of having to look in those boxes. Luckily, the one that had the name Huber on the envelope was one of the first few I looked into. Number 24. Job done.

The dog and I were in and out in no time. I took him in with me to discourage any of the residents who hadn't left for work yet, from going down the stairs to get their daily mail. I did not need anyone interfering with me while I was rummaging through the mail boxes. He was a lovely, friendly, four-legged animal but he had a fixed scary stare at people he didn't know. His brute size was definitely worth waiting for him and me to pass safely by. In fact, an elderly woman had been patiently waiting when we got back to the top of the stairs on our way out.

How Franco never got to be a police dog by profession was a wonder to me. Maybe he was judged to be too mellow in character for law enforcement.

The next morning, early, without Franco as my companion, I drove my car for less than a minute two blocks over. I parked it in a good viewing spot, and snapped my camera at everybody that went in and out on that business day morning. After two consecutive mornings of monitoring the comings and goings of the residents of the complex, I figured out the layout. As is common across Western Europe, the ground floor had no apartments. The apartments on the floor above the ground level were numbered 11 through 19. The first digit apparently indicates the floor number and the second digit signifies the unit number on that level. All I had to do was to focus my attention on the second floor. I quickly located unit 24 and from there on, I was able to determine with certainty the identity of Huber. Managed a few photos of him, even.

He lived alone, wore a smart suit and tie, like someone who worked in a Swiss bank would usually dress. I followed the tram he boarded with my car. It wasn't the tram line I normally took. I spotted him walking down an alley way then entering a classic two-storey older stone building, yards from his stop in town. I parked the car within sight of the structure's entrance. I waited five minutes and saw him appear briefly at the corner window one floor up. I then strolled over to take a closer look. The small gold-plated plaque stated: Swiss Arab Society. The office was part of the Berne branch of Banque Privée de'Neuflize Schlumberger Mallet, a private bank. Its own distinctive double oak doors for the public entrance were further down the main street.

The middle-aged Swiss fellow I was tracking, had a rather unusual dumpy look to his face. Despite his receding hairline and heavy-rimmed spectacles, he had a decidedly Aryan appearance. According to envelopes I'd quickly seen (I'd gone in a second time without Franco), Huber went by several forenames. The ones I'd initially got were Albert, Armand and Ahmed. All started with an A, and were easy to memorise. The last name he used puzzled me greatly. Maybe he had converted to Islam? Certainly, he had a connection of sorts to the Muslim world.

On the fourth day of my investigation, I headed west to Lausanne to check out the four addresses I had for Genoud. I waited until after the morning commuter traffic had eased, reaching my destination within 60 minutes. I was extremely discreet while I snooped around. I changed clothes, and put on a cap. I even varied my strolling style to avoid raising any suspicion. I always parked the car well away from targeted sites and then made my approach by foot. One place within the city limit was indeed an office building, but the index of businesses in the lobby no longer listed Genoud as a leaseholder. Another location, a large rented townhouse, was now advertising its vacancy with a sign planted on the front lawn. The chalets and mansions in the suburbs befitted a wealthy man like him, but apparently, other people now occupied the other two premises. I didn't notice any security precautions of any kind – like cameras, bulky boys hanging about, attack dogs, etc. My search would have been easier had he been listed in the telephone directory. But for obvious reasons he wasn't. And he would never be.

Next, I gave the busy central post office the once over. I took a spot inside where I could stand innocuously without attracting any undue attention. I held a newspaper and pretended to be reading it. It wasn't really a place where I could spend all day hanging about, though. I futilely looked at the employees in the faint hope of identifying the inside person who had furnished some information about Genoud's fully paid-up post box subscription. I quickly conceded that it was an impossible task. I moved on.

The sun was starting to come out for the first time in ages. For me, it was a good psychological sign of positive things to come. I decided to leave the car where I'd parked it and took a taxi over to the impressive Beau Rivage hotel, situated on the shores of Lake Léman. I wanted to get a feel for the place, do a recce. By any means, it was a high-end posh palace surrounded by meticulously maintained gardens. The rather snooty doorman even sniffed at me for daring to wear my jeans and enter his esteemed workplace. At least my pricey jacket, neatly pressed shirt and polished brogues were presentable enough to get me through the hotel entrance. Inside the magnificently kept establishment were a handful of eateries to choose from. I initially settled on seating myself in the reception area and engaged myself in people watching. It was definitely an establishment for the older crowd. I stood out like a sore thumb. Maybe it was the length of my hair. Within a minute or so, a waiter came over and asked me if I'd like to order a refreshment. At the same time, he queried my ability to pay the tab by coughing first and then alerting me that the bill would have to be paid in cash. I took his hint to presumably move on from there. At the same time, I politely asked him to recommend an appropriate restaurant for a light lunch. Betraying his French heritage, Pierre was quick to tell me that his preference was for the French food over the German, Italian and Japanese.

I wandered over to the French restaurant as it was now lunchtime for most guests. I must admit I was damn lucky. Sitting there all alone, at the far end on the sunny terrace, was Genoud! The few others already seated at tables, had all opted to eat inside, in the event of rain. At the sight of my target, my heart started racing. I stood there thinking everybody around me could hear it thundering. I tried not to stare at him. All around me, the sounds seemed to fade. For a few short seconds the world around me had seemingly gone on mute. The maître d' said something to me. I must have responded with a promise to not wear my blue jeans, if I ever paid a return visit to his august establishment. I then added that I would prefer a table outside, please. The brief exchange resulted in finding myself filing in obediently behind the chap towards where Genoud was sitting, drinking what looked like lemon tea. As we passed by his table, he and I actually acknowledged each other with a slight nod. The maître d' dutifully offered a table next to the older man.

A teenaged girl with a dazzling smile then produced the overly-priced menu. I wasn't the only one present representing youth, after all. I ordered a light lunch with sparkling water, and off went the waitress to fetch it for me. As I waited for my order, I opened my jacket to lean back on the chair and crossed my legs. The incredible postcard-like vista in front of me took my breath away. I could see the ferryboat in the distance making its way around the azure lake. Beyond that were the stunning foothills of the white-tipped Alps mountain range. Having taken in everything, I glanced over at the next table and caught Genoud intently looking at me. We acknowledged each other again with a little nod.

"I come here for my *stimmung*, as I see you are doing," he smiled thinly. "But I much prefer the Athenaeum in London to here. You are British, of course."

"I am indeed, sir. I don't believe I have had the good fortune to grace that particular hotel yet. Yes, I know the meaning of that German word. It means, 'understanding the creative mood of the moment'. And you yourself are Swiss?"

He didn't answer the query. Instead, he invited me to join him at his table. I shrugged amiably in agreement and confidently stood up to take the few steps over. He did not stand up as we shook hands, but I did not expect him to do so. His grip, surprisingly, was quite firm. His brown eyes were very piercing, and I felt that he was already evaluating me. I hoped the sheen forming on my forehead wouldn't give away my nervous excitement of having discovered him. He dressed impeccably, hands well-manicured. Spoke accented English well. We bonded fairly quickly despite the massive age gap that existed between us. His appearance was not Nordic by any means. His eyebrows were dark and his greying hair must have been brown or black in his time. Still, I couldn't help but think he looked like a typical Nazi, whatever a typical Nazi is supposed to look like. It must have been the natural air of arrogance about him, which was as chalk and cheese different to the holier-than-thou hotel staff I'd encountered. I got a sense he had grown up affluent.

Maybe he gravitated to me thinking I was a rich kid, like he once was. We chatted about goodness knows what to start with. Mostly small, polite stuff. I hid my hands below the table as they were still quivering slightly. I told myself I'd bring them up once the trembling stopped. There was an eerie yet enigmatic emptiness to him. Closer up, he reminded me of an older version of the fashion designer, Karl Lagerfeld. I had seen his photos in style magazines belonging to my long-term Danish girlfriend. They both had the same demeanour, to my thinking, even though they themselves were two decades apart in age. Maybe it was the German-ish, mixed with the French-ness, outwardly sombre attitudes that Europeans of a certain class projected. It was the arms-length distance they were eager to maintain between them and others despite all the niceties. That is at least until they got to know you better. This assessment does not necessarily imply egotism or even elitism. Genoud's attitudes stem more from his cultural upbringing and the fact that he liked to be in the company of his own kind.

He asked me what I did for a living. I hadn't thought of a cover, since I didn't anticipate this quick joining of friend and foe. "I *used* to work for Forum World Features, a worldwide news service, in London but I was made redundant six months ago," I confidently replied. "Luckily I was given a generous separation package. Fortunately, my family are rather well-off so I've been able to stretch the monies so far. I thought I'd go and visit a few places before beginning to seek employment again," I lied of course, but I hoped I did so convincingly. I had indeed been issued, at one time, a forged FWF accreditation badge that I'd used as cover for SIS courier duties twice, without FWF's express knowledge or authorisation. My real photo was on the badge but I was struggling to remember the name I was given to use. The outfit was really a propaganda machine run by the right-wing establishment to further their cause, until it was forcibly closed down by the newly-elected Labour government.

He never asked me for my name and, interestingly, didn't volunteer his. But he did want to know if I was a Christian, to which I replied in the affirmative. In truth, I was born a Church of England Protestant and became an atheist at a very early age. I didn't mention that last part. My food came to save my bacon while I was thinking of the missing name I had used covertly. In between mouthfuls I politely enquired, "Would you mind awfully if I asked you what you did too, sir, presumably before you retired to a life of luxury?" My now calm palm spread outwardly taking in the hotel's expanse and nearby lake.

He didn't seem to mind the imposition. He must have been transitioning into mentor mode. He leaned forward as if he was keen to talk to a young stranger at length, and offer his refined wisdom. I cursed under my breath that I didn't have a recorder on me.

"Well I am proud to tell you that I am an active financier and investor. I am successful, yet I still regard myself as a work in progress. I happen to know *of* Brian Crozier, too, the person in charge at Forum World Features. Do you have a political leaning, young man?"

A studious fellow to begin with, he now bore deeply into me with his piercing stare. I presumed he was testing me. He wanted to see if his statement about knowing Crozier sparked any reaction on my face. For my part, I remained mum and as controlled as I could be. *It was the best acting I have ever done in my entire life.* "Mr Crozier departed before I did. He was born in Australia, I believe. As far as my political beliefs, obviously I do have them," I responded, "but they may not be the same as yours, whatever they are. Care to tell me where we are going with this discussion while I finish the rest of my luncheon? I'm open minded."

His mention of Crozier's name truthfully rocked me to the core. I was surprised I didn't start stuttering. Forum World Features pushed right-wing conservative viewpoints, which in reality were far removed from my own.

The pretty waitress came by again then. Without asking, she replaced his teapot with another containing freshly boiled water and then took away the empty one. She seemed both attentive to him but comfortable around him. I got the impression from her that he was a regular customer. Several other guests had stepped now onto the terrace to sit at the outside tables. She attended to them as well. Maybe this was where he held court nowadays. And why not. It was, after all, a uniquely impressive spot. I couldn't see any close protection bodyguards around the area. Didn't see any hotel security either for that matter.

Genoud must have talked nonstop for 10 minutes. He showered me with details and hardly gave me the chance to utter a word during his quasi-monologue. I listened attentively. It was as if I had been plucked from the heavens solely for this elderly man to bounce his crazy ideas off. As he kept talking, I couldn't help but think that maybe I was a stooge. But the longer he went on, the more I realised I was incredibly lucky to be in the right place at the right time. Truly a one in a million chance! Because Genoud knew Crozier held similar views to him and was a globally-minded ultraconservative, he must have assumed I was, too. Otherwise, how could I have worked at Forum World Features?

He initially talked in generalities about the coming of the New Order or *Neuordnung*. He expounded on how the borders within Europe would be drastically changed. He didn't quite specify the direction of these realignments. His eyes lit up with fire as time went by. Clearly, he was an unapologetic and divisive fanatic. He was also a fervent Holocaust denier, unsurprisingly. He was emphatically anti-Semitic, repeating often what I considered as despicable lies. From the moment he touched on the subject of Jews, his upper lip snarled and exposed his deep-seated loathing of them. I was stunned he'd talk to someone like me in the extreme manner that he did. I had, after all, just met him. Perhaps he felt removed from us mere mortals. I felt like I was sitting at one end of a tunnel with him at the other end. All the while, the distance between us kept growing and my vision became fuzzier and fuzzier…

In the end his face came back into focus. I was rather proud of myself that I was able to sit through this rant and hear this man spewing a barrage of half-truths and outright lies. On top of that, he openly admitted to realising obscene tax-free profits from a variety of shady and illegal ventures. I must admit that this whole exchange repulsed me no end and left me deeply shaken. He told me he needed reliable, smart minds around him to move some of the blueprints forward. When he concluded, I realised that for a fellow like him, facts can be totally divorced from feelings.

He finished his long-winded diatribe with what could have been a quote from one of Orwell's books, although I doubt it. The quote could have been lifted from *War and Peace* for all I knew. It seemed like I'd heard it before from somewhere. "The last war was not meant to be won, it was meant to be continuous. Hierarchical society is only possible on the basis of poverty and ignorance. This new version is the past and no different past can ever have existed. In principle the war effort is always planned to keep society on the brink of intellectual, emotional or physical reserves of humanity. War is waged by the ruling group against its own subjects, and its object is not just victory over Jews and other undesirable elements, but to keep the very structure of our society intact."

When he stopped to sip his tea and look briefly at his wristwatch, there was a pregnant moment of silence while I digested his words. Most people would have stood up and taken their leave. But I stayed put. I eventually beamed brightly and responded. "Sir, so you are basically an international free agent, involving yourself and your esteemed clients in anything and everything that makes a good profit. I got the impression for a moment that I am being canvassed for a vacant job opportunity. Or were you converting me to a cause? I'm game to make money, even from what I would describe as 'impermissible sources'. Are you offering me a position with you?"

He didn't really answer that directly. Instead he replied, "I see you have a kind of personality that is well-suited to the particular type of work I have in mind."

But exactly what did he have in mind? And what kind of job was he prepared to offer me? I had no idea. I was almost insulted that he thought I shared his despicable views in any way. Sensing that our meeting was coming to a close, I said, "Well I'm interested to know more before making a decision. Is there a way to get in touch with you after I return home to Britain?"

With that, he pulled an embossed business card from his pocket and handed it to me. I had hoped it would be his own, but it wasn't. The card stated, 'Domenique Turrettini, *avocat* (lawyer) for a law firm in Geneva called Poncet, Turrettini, Amaudruz & Neyrod.' "If you do contact me, you will give your telephone number to the personal secretary for Mr Turrettini, and she will quickly make sure I get the message. I will get back to you within the day, wherever you are in the world." I thought Domenique was a woman's name but he confirmed otherwise for me.

"But you haven't given me your own name, sir. How would she know who I am talking about?"

"She will know. I am the only client of the law firm that does business with them in this deliberately anonymous way. The less anybody knows, the better. I never give my name out to anyone until I verify their credentials. I see you do the same, which I like about you. You will say you were the young Englishman that met their client at the Beau Rivage in Lausanne. And you must give them today's date, as well as your phone contact number."

At that very moment, I spotted Huber being escorted in with another suit. I presumed the two guests were being led to Genoud's table by the maître d'. I didn't have time to get nervous. I stood up then to thank the gent and take my leave. When we shook hands he did say, *"Gott mit uns"*, which I knew meant 'God (is) with us' in German. I repeated it back to him, and somehow refrained from clicking my heels.

On the way out, I passed right by Huber but he didn't pay any attention to me. The other bloke was, to my mind, a well-heeled European businessman judging by his appearance. I tried not to rush my exit, by assuming a deliberately relaxed stride. I paid my bill in cash to the cashier at the door and left a tip for the waitress (specifying it was for her). Before I left, I glanced back and saw the three seated at the table, already engaged in deep conversation. I strolled over to the men's loo for a little relief. With a forced smile, I handed the obnoxious doorman, who opened the taxi door for me, a few paltry low-denomination coins. The cab took me back into Lausanne town centre (I checked in the wing mirrors we weren't being followed) and dropped me two blocks away from where I had parked my Audi. I then drove back to Berne in heavy commuter traffic. I must admit I was quite pumped up at having met my main target in the happenstance way I had. I reckoned that I also got to within touching distance of Huber, my secondary target. It was a chance encounter and I had taken maximum advantage of the circumstances.

When I stopped by the office that early-evening to file my findings, Barry was still there. So I filled him in with what had transpired. He was incredulous. He insisted I write my situation report immediately and send it by encrypted telex to SIS HQ at Century House. According to Barry, the very fact that we came back so quickly with a fair amount of usable intelligence, could only enhance our reputation as the consummate professionals we thought we were. On the spur of the moment, and rather uncharacteristically, Barry then invited me for a drink of beer that evening. He was a native of Essex, outside London, and his family were Cockneys originally. He referred to Genoud with the slang term 'corned beef'. He explained it meant 'good with the numbers but not so good with the politics', adding, 'like Toby is too'. I thought it was a fair summary. I thought 'human kaleidoscope' was a better characterisation of him. Genoud clearly had no morals and was coldly calculating. His beliefs and conduct were motivated by deep-seated 100% anti-Zionist positions, while operating in constantly changing symmetrical patterns to deter easy assessments. His various business ventures evolved around where high-risk quick money could be spent and recouped. The end result had to also reflect Genoud's own feral wheeler-dealer instincts.

For his well-established penchant for greed, mixed with animosity, Genoud came, in time, to be known in-house as 'the merchant of hate'.

* * * * * * * * *

I thought that would be the end of that, but it wasn't. Head office replied the next day with a new remit, 'Befriend Huber and Genoud, unearth more dirt. The bank you mentioned finances Islamic fundamentalist activity throughout Western Europe. The law firm you mentioned serves as one of the top legal advisors to the still operational Nazi International apparatus worldwide. This is the first time we have a link between the two. Proceed with haste, but exercise extreme caution.'

Barry and I both read the despatch together as it was printing off the telex machine. We both had a deep intake of breath at the same time.

The first thing I did was check back with SIS where Forum World Features' offices were based before their sudden and forced political closure. I had never been there but now I needed to learn about the place I had supposedly worked at. Just in case. Located at 61-62 Lincoln's Inn Fields, London WC2, it was a handsome four-storey building on the west side of the exclusive square. Nearest underground station: Holborn, served by the Central (red) and Piccadilly (blue) lines. I familiarised myself with the vicinity in my head. It wasn't that far walking east from the capital's theatre district, which I knew quite well.

SIS HQ also confirmed that the false FWF's staff badge I had borrowed twice for other clandestine jobs (briefly used for courier duties in East Germany) belonged to Alan Ling. He was an accredited journalist, who had reported to the top man, Iain Hamilton, who in turn answered to Brian Crozier, before he left. SIS would try to find out the current whereabouts of all three, and then some, in order to best support future action, if any. If the findings failed what we called 'the smell test', then we would abort the idea of my infiltration.

SIS was justifiably concerned that Genoud's people could have taken a picture of me while I sat at his table. In that case, my cover as a Secret Intelligence Service officer could have been severely compromised by any number of likely scenarios. As an example, if the *Bundesnachrichtendienst* (the West German Federal Intelligence Service) had been penetrated by any of Genoud's neo-Nazi sources, it wouldn't have taken them long to establish I was really an SIS officer stationed in nearby Berne. I'd gone through Checkpoint Charlie into East Berlin twice with one of the BND officers from its Cologne office (the SIS had an office there as well), so I was a known entity to the West German security apparatus. That particular operation remained classified.

Frankly, given what skulduggery he was neck-deep in, I was surprised Genoud didn't warrant a state-sanctioned targeted killing (assassination)! It also turned out that in its time, FWF used to be a CIA front company! The SIS worked closely with the Americans, who wanted to know more about Genoud's current activities. SIS sought further protective measures for me from the CIA. The Americans assured us of my safety for the following two weeks. So, we had a fortnight to act while the trio of suspects (Ling, Hamilton and Crozier) were side-tracked. Due to the fact that they were still on CIA's payroll as annuitants (retired agents who remain active on contract), they would be told what to say on the subject, if they were ever approached. Israel's Mossad with whom the US shared select British intelligence, with our prior approval, later came on the scene as well.

The main distinction to differentiate between Genoud and Crozier was that the Swiss was clearly against anything Jewish while the Aussie was pure anti-communist.

After much deliberation, based on everything that was at play on the table, the powers that be at SIS' Century House changed my remit, and settled on the safe middle ground. I would go through the motions of contacting Genoud's people by telephone. I would be tasked with establishing contact with his gang, but I would never get official clearance to meet them again in person. Or as the counsellor in London put it, "You will not enter the lion's den again." Whatever I found out would have to be followed up by others. As I was a Sovbloc controllerate designated operative, my priority was to a more important covert operation rapidly unfolding in Europe: to get China out of their Eastern Europe foothold. I was soon destined to travel to Albania for an unspecified duration. My superiors wanted to ensure that my mission would not be endangered in any way by inadvertently crossing the paths of Huber or Genoud on their home ground in Switzerland, or any of their henchmen for that matter.

For the initial contact, a special line was set-up by HQ to supposedly call the Geneva-based law office from London. It was patched through to Berne, where I was stationed. I spoke in English to a perfunctory Swiss woman who introduced herself as Irmgard. She sounded older, busy and managerial. No time for small talk. "I am from the office of Mr Domenique Turrettini," she had said authoritatively. She professionally noted and repeated back to me what her unnamed client had asked me to do.

As he said he would, Genoud called me back – amazingly, within two hours. We were on a Lausanne-London-Berne call. The recorder was switched on again and a trace for the caller's location was already put in motion. Still no names were used by either of us. We recognised each other's voices, only now his was a straight-to-the-point business telephone voice. I told him I was still interested in working further with him. He responded he had a specific job in mind for me. I asked him to describe the nature of the work. He replied that the job would deal with managing 'bought-in services'. When I asked him to elaborate, he replied it was the business euphemism for 'shadow administration'. I was none the wiser and enquired about the specific requirements for the position. There was some hesitation, like he was deliberating with someone else. On an unsecure open line, he actually reiterated what he'd told me in person 'that he thought I could earn a good salary working for him in Switzerland'…and then he added 'focused specifically in the global funding of freedom fighters' activities' – bingo! – …then a bit more, 'you will learn a lot from me in person'.

Barry was now signalling to end the call, as it was possible, they too could have technical experts who would know where the call was being routed from and to. The longer one stayed on the phone, the easier it would be for competent techies to trace the origin of the call. I told Genoud, once more, I would think about it and come back to him shortly. He ended again on 'Gott mit uns,' which I repeated back to him. I never did contact him.

That same day, a financial expert at headquarters advised me by telex, that the conversation he'd heard obviously indicated the merchant of hate had a secret slush fund at his disposal. He further elaborated that it was a substantial reserve of money used for illicit purposes and was especially available for political persuasion (bribery). These funds had been creamed off from legal funds and placed in sensitive Swiss bank accounts. Specific instructions would likely be given for the in-house compliance clerks to refrain from asking questions regarding the financial affairs of the esteemed client. Therefore, they would not.

The owner of Franco, the dog, had once cynically disclosed to me, "We Swiss are practised in the art of hypocrisy." I could see exactly why he thought that.

We found out later that his incoming call originated from a penthouse that one of Genoud's companies maintained at the Beau Rivage in Lausanne. Within days a team of wiretapping specialists from London arrived and stayed several days there to secretly install monitoring devices in both the suites adjoining it. Later still, continued monitoring of 'chatter' from that hotel number revealed quite a few deep insights over the years. They mostly related to funding of Islamic terrorism. We had implemented the same intercept capability and installed similar equipment used to access communications in the Chinese Embassy in Berne. The hotel's restaurants were also targeted with the same sophisticated listening devices.

Although my role in all this was winding down, I was gratified that my initial humint (human intelligence) work had laid the groundwork for all the technical eavesdropping that followed. I began to refocus on the more pressing issues relating to China's economic invasion of Europe, but I received regular updates on Genoud and Huber through Barry and Toby.

According to SIS files that had been obviously compiled prior to the mid-seventies, Genoud had met Adolf Hitler in Berlin on several occasions. The Nazis introduced him to the Grand Mufti of Jerusalem during the war. The Mufti was an Islamic scholar and a rigid interpreter of sharia law. Grand is the highest rank achievable for a Muslim cleric. The Grand Mufti held his position from 1921 to 1948. He was exiled in 1937 though not dismissed by the British (who controlled the mandate on Palestine then). In his exile, he lived in Germany and worked for the Nazis in disseminating propaganda to Sunni Arab lands. He was paid handsomely for his services. The merchant of hate and the Grand Mufti shared identical fascist views and were fiercely opposed to Zionism. It was rumoured that the Grand Mufti gave the Nazis the idea to commence the Holocaust and build concentration camps. Photographs in the SIS files purport to show Hitler and the Grand Mufti together inspecting several large vacant fields, which gave rise to the speculation. Due to the then discreet ways in which the Swiss financial institutions managed the accounts of foreign clients, the Lausanne-based banker secured exclusive representation of both the Nazi after-war machinery and the successive Grand Muftis' resources. Genoud managed assets in the many millions for his clients, and earned high interest rates for them. When World War II ended, Genoud found himself in the enviable position of not directly reporting to the Nazis anymore. He now had free rein. He continued his role of introducing radical anti-Semitism into Islamic fundamentalism, and provided the funding for such operations.

The merchant of hate was smart but devious. A wrecking ball of a human being, at times his pathologically destructive behaviour classified him as a madman. When I think of him my spine tingles.

I always think, too, of Toby's comment once, circa mid-seventies, as a non-practising Catholic, "What is it that 16 million Jews worldwide have done to deserve the radical attention of two billion Muslims, never forgetting that one billion is one thousand million?"

To which Barry, an atheist like me, replied, "The generations that replaced the Holocaust victims feel their ancestors were meek, and generally went down without putting up a fight. The Jewish people will never allow that to happen to them again, no matter what."

At that time, I remained mum. But later on, I began to reflect on what could have caused someone like Genoud to fill his mind and heart with so much anger and hatred. I came to realise that Genoud and Hitler belonged to a generation humiliated by the terms imposed on the German nation by the victors of the first World War. Armistice negotiations to end the fighting produced a truce that avoided further bloodshed. It also led to the Treaty of Versailles which formally ended the brutal four-year conflict. Both sides had suffered millions of deaths and were eager to stop the carnage. Article 231 of the aforementioned treaty included the so-called war guilt clause that sought to punish the defeated German nation. To most Germans, the heavy reparations imposed on their country, were particularly onerous and vengeful. They could accept that as the losers, they were obligated to pay compensation to the victors. But the restitutions and penalties demanded by the allies were, perhaps, just too harsh. They caused large-scale famine and the starvation of many millions of German families.

Twenty years later, the continuing economic depression led to the rise of the far-right in Germany with Hitler as its leader. He cynically manipulated the suffering masses by promising economic revival along with national redemption. He consolidated his power by ruthlessly eliminating all opposition and then began the plot to take over Europe. One of his early moves in World War II was to invade France.

The lesson learned is it never pays to be short-sighted, as a backlash can happen, and did. This does not excuse the likes of Genoud and Hitler who will always remain monsters.

* * * * * * * * *

The SIS' Berne office started with three of us. The staff was soon expanded to eight, and was later doubled in size. Lots of things happened in Switzerland. "Never start a fart contest with a mixed-race skunk," so concluded a never-thinking-in-the-ordinary Barry Anderson, referring to our side's clandestine role. The increasingly thickening file of the merchant of hate was eventually permanently transferred over to headquarters in London to assume further responsibility for it. From there on, as SIS is so compartmented, I was no longer privy to anything having to directly do with the mysterious François Genoud, who chose to take his own life via euthanasia in 1996. He was never convicted of any crime.

As for his mate Huber, he had indeed converted to Islam. He founded an international banking group in Switzerland called Al Taqwa (means piety or fear of god), which openly billed itself as 'Allah's bank'. That outfit also got 'the works' from the eavesdropping techies who once again came from London. The depository for Allah's objective was to finance Islamic terrorism worldwide. The bank built its portfolio from supporters of the holy cause described internally as Arab liberation. At one point, the bank assets were said to be in the billions of Swiss Francs. Huber was finally arrested in November 2001 for money laundering. He reportedly confessed to helping Hamas write its 36-article covenant. The Preamble to the Charter states: "Israel will exist and will continue to exist until Islam invalidates it, just as it has invalidated others before it".

The merchant of hate and his buddy were true disrupters and incorrigible deniers to their dying days. Both passed away at 81. SIS, CIA and Mossad still have their work cut out for years to come thanks to the likes of Genoud and Huber for their advance work on behalf of their abhorrent clients, the Nazi International and the various Grand Mufti's of Jerusalem.

To this day, no order signed by Hitler has been found ordering the extermination of the Jews. Does this mean he didn't order it to be done?

– Maj. Gen. Moshe Yaalon, AMAN,
Israeli Directorate of Military Intelligence

* * * * * * * * *

Chapter Four

In January 1983, I suddenly and unilaterally decided to quit the SIS. For the past full year, I had been stranded in the madhouse of Beirut. I was imbedded in the Irish contingent of a United Nations force tasked with maintaining peace in rapidly disintegrating Lebanon. I feared for my life. To be honest, I hadn't been exactly in the right frame of mind when I got there. My employer was none too happy about what it considered a snap decision on my part.

Nevertheless, due to my long and sterling service for Britain, I was allowed to retire and collect my well-deserved and hard-earned pension. Of the options available, I chose to receive it in one lump sum. With that money, I went into business with two other men and thus became a one-third owner of a newly-established vinyl record-pressing plant located near King's Cross mainline station in London. I took charge of marketing and sales. A second partner assumed the administration duties, while the third had overall responsibility for production. Each of us had put in one-third of the required investment, so we were equal shareholders.

Within three months of the business launch, the factory had reached full capacity. In fact, the plant was operating around the clock in three 8-hour shifts. The production schedule was filled and the backlog in orders extended for several months ahead. We were positioned to replicate all record formats available on the market at the time: 7", 12" singles and 12" albums. And advantageously, we manufactured the back-catalogue (older titles) for two major labels. So, when demand for new releases slowed down, we filled the void by taking on smaller production runs of golden oldies selected from an extensive list of past hits. To our pleasant surprise, business was coming in faster than we had anticipated. But by the time another calendar quarter had gone by, I began to seek new commercial opportunities and potential entrepreneurial ventures.

One day, while strolling the streets of Manhattan across the pond, I had the fortune of coming face-to-face with a pretty brunette, my soon-to-be wife. She was American-born but her grandparents hailed from Italy. Our courtship proceeded smoothly and for the next six months I became what the airline industry refers to as a NYLON (frequent flyer between New York JFK and London Heathrow or Gatwick). We got married at the end of 1983. We were both in our early-thirties and emotionally ready to take the plunge. I couldn't believe that all these positive developments were taking place within 12 months from the hell of Lebanon. The gods were suddenly smiling on me.

I maintained my regular commute across the Atlantic for another year or so until our successful manufacturing facility was sold at a decent profit. Incidentally, the buyer was the business manager to Bob Marley, the acclaimed Jamaican singer-songwriter, musician and guitarist who died in 1981 at the young age of 36. The reggae artist continued to generate massive royalties even from the grave. And his son, Ziggy Marley, soon forged a money-spinning career in recordings to keep everything going for the family.

At about the same time as the sale, I received my Green Card, which granted me the status of a permanent resident in the US. By then, I had finally spotted a golden opportunity in America. Video rental stores were springing up all across the United States but no one was supplying them properly. I became the first national distributor of pre-recorded movies on videocassettes. I was based in The Bronx, the northernmost borough of New York City. It didn't take long before we opened four other distribution centres across the country. My partner in this business was introduced to me by no other than my mother-in-law. He provided the upfront funds and gave me ample space in a warehouse he owned. All the while, I ran the entire operation without hindrance from him or anyone else.

I had first met this respectable elderly guy on my wedding day. He had introduced himself simply as Uncle Louie. A most humble and easy-going man, I thought. At first, he struck me as a rather timid grocery clerk type but as time went by, I was to be proven totally wrong in my assumption. Frankly, I was more than surprised when Lou expressed his desire to sink as much money into my venture as he did. After all, I was an unknown entity to him, and his largesse was all based on the verbal say-so of a woman he apparently trusted. No business plan was required and none was forthcoming.

In preparation for the enterprise's start-up, I bought substantial inventory, and hired staff. I travelled around the country to meet what the industry called the A-title home video labels, which were owned by the Hollywood studios, and struck supply deals with them. I also met with the heads of smaller independent suppliers of B- and C-movies. The ones we called D's were the badly dubbed ninja tapes from Hong Kong. To be honest, there is some truly dreadful filmed entertainment available out there. The worse it is, the higher the profit margin can be achieved at the wholesale level. I learned that people enjoy kitsch and camp in their downtime. And the poorer the community was, the more often they rented videocassettes.

Not long after commencing operations, I found myself walking in one of the toughest neighbourhood's in The Bronx. On that weekend stroll, I was wearing my knee-length raincoat, with the characteristic black and blue colours of Internazionale Milan football (soccer) club. At some point during my stroll, I felt an urge for a decent cup of coffee. By pure chance, I came across a café with an Italian name prominently displayed on its storefront. As I waited at the counter for service, two gruff men appeared on either side of me. After I ordered my cappuccino from the shifty-looking barista, the sidekicks both insisted on picking up the tab. Forget *The Godfather*. This was more a scene from an imaginary and yet-to-be released film tentatively titled *The Oddfather*.

Puzzled by their unexpected act of generosity, I asked them why I was being accorded such courtesies. Neither one directly responded to my query. Instead, one of them silently motioned I should follow him down an unlit hallway to the back of the building. The other chap filed in right behind me. I could feel him breathing on my neck. I had no idea what was going on. Fearing some kind of mischief, or even a daylight ambush with potentially ominous consequences, I steeled myself to smash them both with a quick karate move I knew quite well. But before anything happened, a door ahead opened and a dim light flooded the corridor. Inside, more than a dozen men filled the room. They were clearly engaged in illegal gambling. The moment they saw me at the door, they stopped in unison what they were doing to stare intently at me, a total stranger in their midst. For them, my blue and black outfit could have looked like the outfit of a feared undercover cop. For a few long seconds, you could have heard a pin drop. As if on cue, the two fellows who had escorted me into the room pointed at a huge Inter Milan flag spread across the entire far wall. In an instant, all the pent-up tension evaporated. We all became like old friends and patted each other on the back. After a short while, my two hosts took me back to the front of the shop to allow me to finish my rapidly-cooling down free coffee.

While sipping from my cup, I learned from these geezers that customers of illegal numbers joints routinely frequent street-level storefronts like this one, to place their bets on a three-digit number. I was to discover that the winning numbers are actually determined by the last three digits of the total proceeds collected from a particular racetrack on a given day. It could be horses, greyhounds or go karts. The proceeds from each race were always published in newspapers the next morning and could be added up to arrive at a total. But it was the ending three numerals in the final figures that these illicit punters paid attention to, to find the winning numbers. Every in and out transaction was cash only – no taxes paid to the state's coffers.

It was only when I got out of the coffee shop that I realised what Uncle Louie was actually doing with our quickly reached deal. I'm by nature very karmic so I felt that the wee exercise I'd been through was a message for me from the divinities, whoever and wherever they were. And old man Lou had no qualms whatsoever admitting his activity. In fact, he confirmed it immediately after I had confronted him. He called his retail fronts "banks" (code for illegal betting parlours). He also confided in me that he and his brother collected between $13 and $15 million every year from 250 locations spread across all five boroughs of New York City, including 90 in The Bronx alone. I could see how the money he had advanced for my business amounted to chickenfeed in the grand scheme of things. His real intention all along was to leverage our legally-operated company and use it as a front to expand his illegal gambling operations across the country, via newly-opened video stores. It turns out he was a Genovese crime family associate and was protected by the mob. Did I think to pull out by reneging on our agreement? No. But other ideas hit me.

Not long after my little encounter with Louie and his admission about his gambling operations, I received a late-night call from him, with a request for a 'favour'. He asked me to go to a notoriously bad area of the South Bronx in order to meet a hood named Vito, whom I would recognise. No further explanation was given to me at that time. In those days, I drove a flashy and distinctive yellow Mazda RX7 sports car. Given the vague nature of the assignment and as a reasonable precaution against mischief, I parked my beloved toy several blocks away, in a spot where I could make a quick getaway if the situation demanded it. I might add that it was bucketing down with rain and I had to fork out $10 to a bunch of ballsy teens who approached me and promised to look after my wheeler till I got back... I could only imagine the dire consequences had I not agreed to their terms and refused to hand over the 'protection money' they politely demanded from me. With a rich dose of apprehension, I then walked the distance to my pre-arranged appointment. I was quite aware of the risk of getting mugged for being a white man in the wrong place and at the wrong time in a black man's neighbourhood. But I had a mission to accomplish.

As I approached the meeting place, soaked to the skin, Vito betrayed his hiding spot in a doorway by the puffs of smoke emanating from his cigarette. He seemed genuinely surprised that I had spotted his ugly mug with so little effort. I was going to say he was no oil painting to look at but thought better of it. Anyhow, he told me to stay put and keep my trap shut. It seemed that only he would do the talking. Ten long minutes later, and out of the gloom, a dark saloon with four black dudes in it, slowly rolled up. We revealed ourselves and made our presence known. As instructed, I stood quietly behind Vito with my hands in my pockets. They exchanged some pleasantries and then my guy gave them a briefcase, presumably crammed with greenbacks. They left soon afterwards.

Nothing more to it than that. In the morning, Lou enquired how the affair went. I told him these precise details while stifling coughs, adding that

Vito could use some deodorant. He seemed happy with the outcome but I was none the wiser as to what had actually transpired, other than I was there just to witness the transaction between Vito and an unspecified client. I never mentioned to the old man that Vito revealed to me he was a *capo decina* (head of a 10-man internal group of Mafia soldiers). I could only guess where his underlings were that night.

The off-script and unofficial version in the deluge of biblical proportion of the previous night was right at when my watch's hands had overlapped at 10:54. Vito had stiffened when the suspected cloned vehicle (false licence plates) had switched off its headlights and cruised in darkness the last block to our spot. That action of theirs told me the missing heavy brigade of Italians were probably on standby nearby, and the black street guys knew it. No proof. Just my instincts telling me. Once that beam went blank, I immediately began to scan the murky rooftops for any mischief in the making. When I finally went to collect my car afterwards, one of the street kids wisecracked, "Man, the 'hood is chockfull of whiteys tonight!" I wondered who else had entrusted their cars to their care! I was left in no doubt that these teens were the lookouts for their elders as well. This kind of situation happened a lot in Belfast and Beirut so why should The Bronx be any different.

On another occasion, Lou literally ordered me to forget the plans I had for the next morning. I simply shrugged and proceeded to do as he instructed. He told me to advance unlimited credit to 'Fernandez', the man I was scheduled to meet in the Colombian environs of Corona in Queens. Again, I parked my sports car a number of blocks away, this time in broad daylight. As I turned the corner of the designated street, I passed four Hispanic hoods seated in a car, wearing baseball caps and sunglasses, looking cool. I walked to the other end where another four sat in a vehicle, also sporting headgear and shades. Then I calmly went to the middle spot between the two vehicles and very soon a black stretch limo rolled up. I was beckoned to get in, and off we went for a ride – sandwiched by the same two cars. Inside was 'Fernandez', who had no problem telling me they'd done a deal with the Genovese crime family to run numbers through video stores in the Spanish-speaking areas of Queens, Brooklyn and Staten Island. Somehow the deal excluded Manhattan and The Bronx but I didn't bother to ask him why. It was what you call a Mafia-style 'licensing agreement', verbal only.

Once again, Lou asked me the next morning how my day before had gone. I gave him the full account without missing out one iota. By now, old man Lou was getting a handle on my dark humour and enquired about how the Colombian had smelt (because I'd mentioned that the time before that Vito stank). I was surprised he had actually remembered my tongue-in-cheek complaint. So, I told him with a straight face the name of the expensive perfume the man was using, and that it was as pleasant as could be. Seemed to make him smile on this occasion.

After some time had passed and 'Fernandez' had paid his bills on time, I introduced my Queens sales representative to them. He was a hard-working Nigerian-born chap, who had once served in the army over there. One evening the African lad called me at home to say he was in a depot where 'Fernandez's associates stored the videocassettes...and did I know they kept assorted carbines and other weaponry in there? I cut him off at once and told him we'd meet to talk about this in the morning at the office, which we did. For a former corporal in the Nigerian army he knew what he was looking at, I must say. But he wisely refrained from ever mentioning the subject again to me. This is the way it is on the streets of New York City, a whole new way of conducting 'business' and modus operandi uniquely tailored for the mean streets of its five boroughs. I was learning fast.

These two 'diversions' are the only courtesies Uncle Louie asked me to undertake on his behalf and in support of his side of operations. Otherwise, I was left alone to get on with what I did best. Perhaps it was an initiation rite to test my skills and trustworthiness? Or maybe he just liked the idea of an Englishman in the family. After all, he collected signed works by noted book authors from my country by the dozen, as a hobby. At least, that's what he claimed to me once.

What my mum-in-law, old man Louie and his cronies never knew though was my own dirty little secret. Unbeknownst to them, they had got in bed with a former covert action intelligence officer from the British version of the clandestine unit of the CIA (Central Intelligence Agency). I elected to keep my mouth shut about this improbable turn of events. By pure happenstance, due to family connections, and despite never undergoing an initiation ceremony, I had inadvertently become the newest member of La Cosa Nostra (this thing of ours) – the all-encompassing descriptive for belonging to the mafia, which Italian-American bad boys often referred to instead as "Our Thing". These last words were usually accompanied by a shrug or a smirk. From early on, I had promised myself to carry on doing my own thing, along the lines of my previous business in London.

Fortunately, I was able to take advantage of this unlikely springboard to create spinoffs related to the home video industry. I organised an annual trade exhibition (business convention) in Atlantic City for the now burgeoning pre-recorded tape industry. I began a Spanish-language national video distributorship, a music video programming service, and a free monthly consumer newspaper promoting films coming out on videocassettes. They all evolved into successful niche businesses. They were not directly connected to the original company set up by Louie and me. He knew about their existence but never showed any interest to be involved in them. He had no reason to be. He was deeply involved in his own lucrative, albeit illegal, business activities.

* * * * * * * * *

Any distributorship worthy of its name, needs a sales force consisting of dynamic, can-do types to serve as the foot soldiers for the operation. They are, by and large, young men and women who measure their success by their ability to close deals. Among them all, my New Jersey salesman stood out head and shoulders above the rest of them. Let's call him Elie. He was a young man of Lebanese descent who for reasons unknown to me chose the hard-to-forget street name of The Emperor. During the early days of setting up my business, this uniquely engaging fellow popped out of nowhere. On a bright early morning, he brazenly knocked on the warehouse door and asked me for a job. I already had someone assigned to the territory so I could not immediately offer him one. But he persevered and came out with his own optimistic idea. He asked for two cases of merchandise to be provided without any down-payment on his part.

My instinct told me to gamble on him. Upon proof of ID, I agreed to give him the goods on a consignment basis. The next day, Elie was back with the cash owed, having sold all the tapes. But now, he wanted four additional cases of product in good faith. Again, he returned with the money the next day. This unlikely credit arrangement went on for some time until the bookkeeper advised me that the part-time guy was actually selling more than the full-time sales representative. So, I called in the full-timer to discuss this issue. He sheepishly admitted he was holding two jobs. That wasn't stipulated in the employment contract, so I fired him on the spot. Elie took his place the next day on terms that included a base salary plus commission.

Elie's exploits are many. I learned from the intrepid self-styled Emperor of an incident that occurred while I was in Las Vegas on a business trip. At the time, Elie was still a free-lancer and not yet officially on board. As was his routine, he arrived one morning, at the office/warehouse expecting the same credit arrangement I had afforded to him. Since I was called out of town suddenly, my staff sent him to Louie. Louie sat Elie down in his office and heard him out. He then reached into a drawer and slid a book across the desk to Elie. Apparently, the front cover stopped the right way around for Elie to see it was about 'the history of the Mafia'. Using his most sinister voice, the older man told Elie to open it at a specific page and to read out the paragraph at the bottom left. Elie did so. The text essentially identified Louis as the underworld boss of The Bronx for the Genovese crime family. Elie said he shrugged in acceptance of the fact and politely handed the hardcover back. Then Louie said to him, "If you f*** me you're a dead man." But Elie got his wish on that day and walked away with everything he came for. The older man later confirmed he had met the upstart.

On another occasion, two of the Hong Kong martial arts stars on the shitty D-tapes came into town accompanying the label owner, Elie begged me to allow him to take one of them, the bald Shaolin monk – a celebrity among black clientele – around New York City's poorer southern 'hoods in Queens and Brooklyn for the day. Meanwhile, the owner and the other star came with me on a grand tour of The Bronx. All I know is The Emperor and The Monk had a good day out together, as we did. However, a few days later I received a surprise invoice in the mail for $3,000, courtesy of the NYPD (New York Police Department), for 'unscheduled crowd control and traffic enforcement'. Evidently, Elie had taken the Chinese chap into

Manhattan's largest video store on the way back to the office and caused a stampede of fans eager to see the kung fu celebrity from up close. With the NYPD calling, I obviously had to settle the bill. But the mini-tour generated a massive promotional bonanza. The store was part of a national chain and the buyer, based on what he saw was going on, ordered enough merchandise to cover the expenses that Elie inadvertently ran up – ten times over.

Flushed with bonuses on payday, Elie insisted on taking me out for dinner into the city. So off we went to a uniquely fancy restaurant frequented by famous names. We went there on two separate occasions and on the spur of the moment. I don't know how many people can say they've run into the singer Billy Joel but Elie and I came across him on both occasions. A minor miracle really. And the rock star acknowledged us the second time with a wave, which made Elie's day.

And then one day, Elie disappeared off the face of the earth, leaving no trail behind. I went to his apartment in New Jersey and knocked on his door. I tried to reach him by phone but there was no answer either. In short, nobody knew of his whereabouts and a missing person report was filed with the local police. Six weeks later he showed up out of the blue, much like he did the first time I met him. This time, his hair was very long. He innocently came to claim his job back, much to my chagrin.

"Where the f*** have you been all this time?" I demanded to know.

Came the answer, "C'mon, boss, I got bored – so I decided to go on a boat trip down the Amazon River."

Then he proceeded to show me an array of photographs of him posing with head-hunters, pygmies, a large piranha he caught fishing, and an assortment of other mementos from Brazil. I should mention that both his ears were now pierced with umpteen gold rings hanging down from his lobes. Fortunately, no tattoos adorned his face. Yes, I gave him his old position back and he continued where he left off like nothing had happened.

Then one day a few years later, a major multinational corporation from America's heartland, which traded on the NYSE (New York Stock Exchange), showed interest in my businesses. After a few go-arounds, they made me an offer I simply couldn't refuse. In due time, I sold my stake in several registered entities to the conglomerate for cash. On the day I received that bank transfer, I resigned from the company Louie and I had started. It was all his to keep, no problem. I was out of his hair; and he was out of mine.

As for Elie, on the day I sold the company, he quit. Decades later he resurfaced as a thriving art dealer of photographic art. He had married and had a son, and had his own galleries in Dubai and Doha in the Middle East. Somehow, I wasn't surprised at his success. I wish there were more people who espoused the creed, 'Why be boring? Be different.'

* * * * * * * * *

Fast forward from 1989 to 1997. My mother-in-law called me in Belize, a place I had been living in since 1995. She relayed to me some widely reported news in the US media that was not known to me at the time. According to these TV reports, Uncle Louie, his brother and some 25 other individuals had been arrested by the NYPD following a wide-ranging investigation. The enquiries that had started two years earlier included court-ordered wiretaps. From her descriptions, I was pretty sure that the Federal Bureau of Investigations (FBI) had to be intimately involved in the case.

In her defence, the lady claimed she had no prior knowledge of his local and national illegal activities. But then to be honest, Italian-American womenfolk had the loyal presence of mind to never question what kind of skulduggery their menfolk and kin were up to. Fortunately, from an early time I had cottoned-on to what was happening, and elected to stay mum throughout to avoid any entanglement with Lou's side of the operation. I mean, realistically, how long did Louie and his sibling think they could skirt around the law and not pay taxes to the IRS, the Internal Revenue Service, on their obscenely high profits? *The government always requires a piece of the action, otherwise you will face their wrath for not sharing your profits with the authorities.*

During my time in 'Noo Yawk Shitty', skirting around the fringe of this organised racket, I learned some Italian words, and became somewhat familiar with the culture they brazenly imported from their native Sicily into America. The word Mafia has its roots in the term *mafiusa*, which in Sicilian means 'swagger' or 'boldness' (but in the US the word morphed into mafioso). These modern-day gangsters felt they were emulating the medieval order, whereby a noble family more or less served as the benevolent ruler of local villages across southern Italy. The trouble is in the modern world of greed and corruption, the benign leaders of yesteryear evolved into powerful crime syndicates, just like in Britain in the early-seventies. They were involved in pyramid schemes, rigged bids, bribery, extortions, and the like. More often than not, these activities were accompanied by the threat of violence, actual bloodshed and in wipe-outs. It was only a matter of time before these outlaws got caught. That's when they faced the choice between long prison sentences or electing to testify against The Mob. In return, they were promised to enter the US government's Witness Protection Program. In reality, it wasn't much of a choice. *There was, perversely, a downside to the upside. If there was not going to be a trial it meant you were almost certainly going to be a dead man anytime soon anyway. The Mafia doesn't like betrayal by its members any more so than intelligence services do.*

* * * * * * * * *

Looking back, I can only smile to myself when I think about those overweight, gum-snapping, shady mobsters and corrupt Irish-American cops that showed up in Louie's warehouse on pay-off days. Many of the Anglophiles had Sal or Vinny attached to their names. The boys in blue, however, usually went by Liam or Pat. They were to the last one of them incorrigible Anglophobes. They had no qualms regularly professing their ignorance and loathing of the British straight to my face. They left no doubt that their unequivocal sympathy was with dissident republicans (also known as nationalists) in the Ireland of their forefathers.

To be honest, I'd never faced racial hatred of any kind before. In this instance, I could only presume it was a structural form of cultural hatred, since it manifested itself as white against white. As matters stood, I wisely failed to mention I wasn't a Catholic either. That would have infinitely aggravated my situation vis-à-vis these heirs of the bastard Fenians (members of the ancient Irish Republican Brotherhood). They, of course, had no clue I'd pretended to be one of them in the Lebanese civil war. Their traditional opposition, the Protestants (Prods), called themselves unionists or loyalists. Both denominations are Irish-Christians, too. But many of New York City's finest weren't even aware that the emerald island over the pond was made up of two countries either, or they didn't want to know.

And the pea-soup fog gets worse. I don't know if it's dotage (senility) or they are simply dolts (stupid), but this strange collection of wise guys became even more intolerable when inebriated. They used to gently slap me with an open cigar-stained palm on my cheek to showcase their toughness. All the while they waved their pistols around in my face, "Hey kid, ever seen a firearm before?" For my part, I would respond all wide-eyed and pretend that I hadn't! With that, they would all roar with laughter.

It's not hard to kill a man. It's harder to live with his death.

I guess everything worked out okay in the end for me. I got out at the right time. It was an episode in my life where my real family life was involved in The Family *(La Famiglia)*. From my perspective the term is nothing more than an invented name in Hollywood films for these overhyped gangsters. But at all times I observed the rules and unspoken code of loyalty. I met bosses *(capos)* and all those in-between down to the ordinary members or soldiers *(soldati)*. I didn't rat on anybody and at the end of the day I took the honourable way out.

Mind you, dealing with these street-wise Catholic Italian-American and Irish-American characters was infinitely easier than tackling those feral hoards in Hezbollah or the Palestine Liberation Organisation that I ran into in Beirut not too many moons earlier. Those wild-eyed Muslim goons, who hailed from the ghettos and refugee camps, could really scare the life out of even the most courageous of us. At least life and family stood for something with the American mobsters, as it did with the Provisional Irish Republican Army's gunmen.

But the Arab zealots were fighting for a god of a different kind. They believed that when they died in battle for Allah they would be welcomed into Paradise with open arms. They would gain the right to unlimited sex with 72 virgins in the afterlife. It was just religious wacky stupid and banal stuff that got preached into their heads and pants. To these misguided criminals, murder and assassination was a blood sport enjoyed in wolf packs. Killing kids was okay. It's something the rest of us abhor, regardless of how tough we think we are. Though, come to think of it, we English called fox hunting a sport, sitting safely on horses, while letting the foxhounds do the bloody killing of another animal…

The bottom line is, at that stage of my life, I had started a family in the United States. I was determined to leave all the shit of the Middle East behind me. I never ever wanted to see a shooter again, hold one, or fire one. So, I dealt with these encounters by just smiling gently in their bellicose faces and simply moving on. I was determined to take things nice 'n' easy. At the same time, I was also learning that trying to remain truly neutral and not be intolerant, proved to be challenging in the insolent sense. *I was confronted with unrelenting blind hatred and ignorance from people who twisted the facts to suit their wrong-headed sets of belief. But to contradict this, I have always known the other side would be willing to misinterpret to their advantage. It's a human trait.*

I have to admit that NYC is not really my cup of tea – not my kind of place. For starters, it has a high concentration of aggressive cyclothymic (minor manic-depressives) types that forces you to always have to be on your guard. I am of the beach bum, bohemian, surfing equation, mostly free as the wind. So I preferred the likes of laid-back Southern California's wide-open places. It has always bothered me when people can't say hello to or smile at close neighbours, too, which tends to happen in big concrete metropolises. I really felt alienated there, despite being surrounded by millions. My soul felt manacled by the relentless march to materialism's tune. There's more to living life than that.

Perhaps one of the most fragrant cases of irrational and overt hatred I personally encountered in America was when I played one season for an Irish pub football (soccer) team called Shamrock in Queens, NYC. All the lads bar a Brazilian and myself were Irish, mostly from the southern half of Ireland. They were all decent fellows, except for two surly brothers from Northern Ireland whom I noticed never ever passed the ball to me. This act went on unnoticed by the others for thirty-something matches until we reached the last game, the cup final. With only a few minutes left in the game, one of the brothers should have passed me the ball to score the winning goal from a few yards out. But he miserably failed to do so. Asked by the coach in the dressing room afterwards to explain his actions, he simply responded, "Because he's an Englishman." I can confirm right there and then the two brothers got their heads well and truly kicked the shit out of by their own islanders. Funny way to accomplish my vendetta in the end, really.

Then I joined Lazio in The Bronx, introduced to the president of the Italian-American *calcio* (football) club by my mother-in-law. Named after the big professional team of the same name in Rome, staunchly followed by the *fascisti* (fascists). I only played a season for them, too, because the wall-size photo of Benito Mussolini in the dressing room doing the Nazi salute was too much to bear. I later found out that the US had openly offered safe haven to thousands of fascists after World War II ended. Not only Italians but Germans (Nazis) as well. This discovery reminded me of my early-days at the SIS' Special Political Action section. I have yet to get to the bottom of why the US and UK governments got into bed with such types. Did they really despise the leftists that much to steer their respective nations towards oppressive capitalism?

Not long after I got married, I received a phone call in Manhattan from the London Controlling Station. This is the joint operation between the Security Service, coined as MI5, whose patch was domestic Britain, and the Secret Intelligence Service (SIS), known as MI6, whose remit related to matters outside the British Isles. Respectively they are the UK's versions of the FBI and CIA.

I was requested to meet two intelligence officers, one each from MI5 and MI6. There were due to arrive at New York City's John F. Kennedy (JFK) airport on a British Airways flight. For all expenses covered, but not my time, I was asked to escort them for two days and two nights for three appointments with well-meaning Irish-American charitable organisations. These altruistic groups were raising monies for various causes in both Northern Ireland, which belonged to the UK, and in the Republic of Ireland, also known by its Gaelic name, Eire, which was its own country. The problem was that all the funds were being diverted to an account at a particular branch of the Bank of Ireland that was used by the terrorist Provisional Irish Republican Army. PIRA were also known as the Provos. (In 1969 the IRA split into the Official IRA and the Provisional IRA. The latter being the more dominant faction. Years later PIRA separated into the Continuity IRA and the Real IRA. Most observers would agree there wasn't much to differentiate between them. All these splinter groups were against Britain's control of Northern Ireland and the Protestants perceived persecution of Catholics.)

So I drove them in my wife's SUV, given that my sports car only had two seats. Straight from JFK we hit the New England throughway to Boston, some half a day's drive north. They thought I was pulling their legs when I mentioned Massachusetts was not a state but a commonwealth, nevertheless it is.

Up there, we met two of the charities, with the third scheduled back in New York City's The Bronx the next day. The persons who attended these meeting seemed outwardly wary of us trio of Englishmen. But the duo I'd collected from Britain had plenty of both documentary and photographic proof to present. It clearly showed where the misappropriated, or appropriated by default, dollars ended up. One specific bank transfer had directly paid for a car bomb in Belfast that killed many innocent civilians, including children. As the meeting went on, one Irish-Yank committee member became indignant at our presentation. After proffering apologies upfront, we produced a gory close-up picture for inspection of a once young girl wearing a pretty dress. But she had no head attached to her torso. The grisly display finally did the trick on the resentful chap. His reddish face turned ashen in our presence and only a handkerchief prevented him from gagging. Killing kids bothered Christians (unlike another religious denomination).

And just before The Bronx meeting, I told the other two about my time playing football for Shamrock. I told them that I suspected some local Irishmen may recognise my face. On hearing this, one of the British officers instructed me never to say I lived in Mount Vernon, a town just north of The Bronx. Reason being that Mount Vernon in Belfast was a Protestant stronghold! I don't know if this was intended as a dry-humoured joke at the time. I do know it only took a little wrong word to trigger Irish-Americans to find fault with anybody who hailed from Britain, especially England.

In the end, we could not prevent them from continuing to send money to Ireland. But we requested that the funds not be sent to that particular bank account anymore. As it turned out, I was later informed those wire transfers ceased to a trickle almost immediately. However, they were soon replaced by other clandestine means. There was an increase in flights booked on Aer Lingus into Dublin by cops with Irish names holding US passports. Each carried roughly $9,500 in undeclared cash in bags ($10,000 being the declarable limit). The ultimate recipients remained PIRA, still, for many years to come. It was a classic example of *Schlimmbesserung* (doing something to make it better but actually making the situation worse).

For me, the really bad news – the British intel guy from SIS reliably informed me at JFK when he was leaving – was that SIS were seriously considering resurrecting much of the (closed in 1974) Special Political Action's illegal capabilities with a newly named unit, which they did eventually in 1993 and it was called I/Ops or Information Operations.

So nothing really changes in the bigger scheme of things. What goes around; comes around again.

* * * * * * * * *

Yes, well, quite a lot of 'irregular events' happened in my time in the US. I'm perfectly content I cannot go there anymore as I'm now *persona non grata* (Latin for: person not appreciated) for alleged terrorism offences. Quite typical of how big government in the States works. What's interesting is for all the things one could say prejudicial about me, there is absolutely no validity to the misguided ruling. In fact, the opposite is the case. I can only close my eyelids momentarily and sigh. Life goes on. It's a perfect example of how the law can be an arse.

Note: The Supreme Court of the United States, *Holder*, Attorney General et al v. *Humanitarian Law Project* et al, Washington, DC, number 08-1498. Argued 23 February 2010. Decided 21 June 2010. The Obama administration's appointee, Elena Kagan, argued that if you talk to terrorists and terrorist organisations it is no longer "material support", instead expanding it to *"you are guilty* of giving material assistance to terrorist groups", even when in reality the aim of such assistance in my case was attempting to *solve crises* through nonviolent negotiation to save hostages lives. It was a closed-minded executive decision without review and without recourse. The judgement was applied straightaway by the FBI despite the existence of a sensitive persons' information agreement between nations that relates to the sharing of data about the diplomatic corps serving overseas, which includes declared intelligence officers. Fact: the US database has a mind-boggling 1.2 million names suspected of so-called terrorism-related involvement.

To conclude on this subject matter, in a taken hostage situation negotiators had to submit to the operations centre a LQE (longitudinal qualitative evaluation), a measure of change in the state of affairs since the last time on-site at the location, in terms of LQE, LQE+ or LQE- (same, plus or minus). No change, or an improvement, meant we would give it more time for success to materialise, while a deterioration required a change of strategy. The SIS, Title 10 (operations for the military) and some police forces in the UK use LQE in radio reports from the field, so there's a regular brief for others involved to know what's happening or not happening. Clearly the US' ICE (Immigration and Customs Enforcement) doesn't do any form of LQE as it would require time for the person charged to prove one's innocence or guilt. Instead it is a policy of a flat yes or no, black or white, in arriving at all-encompassing concrete final lecisions. Likewise, the FBI's goal is always to obtain a conviction. In general, that's where Uncle Sam goes wrong. No broader thinking ahead of what may be around the corner; it's got to be done the narrow path way, right now.

What's true and what's right are different.

* * * * * * * * *

Chapter Five

Gracias por una vida interesante que me ha dado tanta variedad.
(Thank you for an interesting life which has given me so much variety.)

For a stretch of five years (1995-2000), I lived in Belize on the exotic atoll of Ambergris Caye. This tiny island is situated off the eastern coast of Central America. It is best known for its barrier reef of living coral, a wonder of nature with few parallels. The nearby mainland to which the isle belongs, was once known as British Honduras. Way back when, the British appropriated the land from Guatemala without offering any compensation in return. Before that, the buccaneers in the Caribbean, many of them English, adopted the island as their haven, and for centuries stashed their loot in these hideaways. Naturally, they were keen to protect the pirated goods from the prying eyes of the armadas patrolling the high seas. It's now a British territory, sometimes known as 'the Switzerland of Americas', surrounded by Spanish-speaking dominions.

The official language today is indeed English, but the large majority of its inhabitants still speak Spanish, as well as patois and creole (there are subtle differences between the two French dialects). Lots of Americans live there now, having brought with them their own version of my native tongue. They added many abbreviations and acronyms into the mix, creating a unique dialect that I like to call 'Americanese'.

In order to encourage tourism and in particular to attract free-spending North American holidaymakers, the coastal areas and the 400 islands sprinkled along the barrier reef were renamed as the Western Caribbean. The former name of Central America (that was once shortened to CA) created much confusion. The term CA became an issue when post mailed from the US regularly ended up in California or even in Canada before being returned or forwarded to its intended destination. Not surprisingly, instead of taking one week for an envelope to arrive at the post office of collection, this mislabelling error often caused a delay of many months in the mail delivery. I won't even get into the further mess that was caused when Ambergris Caye decided at one time to truncate its name to AC, the reversal of CA… Go figure!

The paradise-like setting had its downside, though. Getting the local workers to come to work on time was nearly impossible, since nobody wore watches. But these kinds of self-inflicted administrative snafu were typical in those early days. I attribute them largely to the birth pangs of a newly independent nation. The upside is that Belize enjoyed all the national holidays of Great Britain, the United States, Canada, and of course, its own native stay-at-home days. Needless to say, the populace thus enjoyed many days off annually on full pay!

During my time in Belize, Guatemala, our miffed next-door neighbour would, every year without fail, muster some of their troops on Belize's western frontier. The mobilisation of their armed forces was to remind us all that they lay claim to our territory. Depending on which regiment was currently training in the jungle on the mainland at the time, the British Army would send in variously the Green Berets (Royal Marines), The Black Watch or the Gurkhas to quell the 'hiccup'. Later, after the so-called revolt had been quashed, the soldiers would be rewarded with time off on the island where I lived. So, before the days of the internet, I got to meet many of these warriors. In the additional absence of daily newspapers, I got timely updates from them on current world affairs and then some…the non-conformities as it were.

One such interesting snippet that drew my attention in a roundabout way related to the whereabouts of the former Grand Vizier of the Ku Klux Klan. He had been reported missing since 1984 in the US, and in half a shake he was suddenly a new neighbour of mine. I met him a few times but

I never let on to him that his presence on the island was well-known to those active in international security. You should know that Belize is overwhelmingly made up of people of Mayan descent, Mestizos, those of Spanish heritage, and many whose forefathers were slaves from Africa – mulattoes, quadroons and octoroons. So, for the leader of the 'White Racial Brotherhood' to show up and take residence on a racially diverse island was peculiar to say the least.

The flip side to the mix of colour was the sex tourism. Apparently, in keeping with the ethos of the liberal agenda, young, good-looking German dolls and some older overweight American matrons, both sets white, chose to come to the Belizean islands. They intended to sleep with as many 'well-endowed' black men as they could for the duration of their stay. I should add that while the younger gals received the 'services' of the black stallions for free, the older women actually had to pay for their sexual escapades. You couldn't help but notice that the local lads passed around their 'clients'. In the end, everybody benefitted. After all, Ambergris Caye is only 25 miles long by less than a mile wide, with the small town of San Pedro in the centre. It's like living in a tinted glass bowl surrounded by blue sky and blue water. I might add that the air could get very blue, too, with all these goings-on. The famous Blue Hole was also very close by.

Then there was the open secret of cocaine bales from Colombia destined for North American noses transiting through the hundreds of drop-off points along the 185-mile barrier reef. Payments would be sent from Belize, through trusts registered offshore, to the producers' pockets in South America. Up to $4 billion of dirty money is circulating the planet every year. Belize is one spoke in the wheel making it go around. To all of us who lived there, our eyes knew what was going on, and who was behind the racket, but we kept our mouths shut because we didn't want to die prematurely from non-natural causes. For the majority it was a case of live and let live, knowing those that fought against the scum of the earth were doing their best to stem the tide.

Despite the ill-repute that Belize had unwittingly earned for itself, still to this day, it makes the best tasting beer, coffee and *creviche*, a marinated raw seafood. Living life on the edge of the world certainly wasn't boring!

Apart from my almost daily scuba diving, in search of my harpooned snapper lunch, I occupied the large majority of my time there with three main activities:

First and foremost, I took my quest to be an author seriously. You aren't an authority until you are published. Writing and editing the manuscript for my first book, *NOC – Non-Official Cover: British Secret Operations*. Monday through to Friday I would wake up at dawn, have breakfast, and then start typing straight into the computer. Occasionally I would forget to have lunch but by 4 PM I'd be heading out of the door to undertake football training sessions. Saturday was my self-imposed day off and Sunday was game day, home or away.

The second activity, as I've hinted, involved coaching the local football club (only the US, Ireland and Australia refer to this sport as soccer – three out of a whopping 211 nations on the planet). The club went by the name San Pedro Dolphins and it was affiliated to one of the two main national political parties. Aside from that, I later organised a new football club with no connection to any political entity. It was called Ambergris Caye Turquoise, which soon was abbreviated to 'La Turquesa', which is The Turquoise in Spanish. It was named for the colour of the 40-feet of water that separated the land from the coral reef. Amazingly, 1,000 boisterous fans would regularly show up for a home game. Quite a spectacular attendance when you consider that the entire local population was barely 5,000 at the time. Some intrepid fans would even sail in from nearby islands to watch the game, especially the reggae-loving Rastafarians from Caye Caulker. For away games, we travelled crammed into a small boat to the mainland. A trip of two to three hours one-way, depending on how far we were going to play.

And if that wasn't enough, I also volunteered to coach the national team, gratis. Such were the finances of the FIFA-member Belize Football Association that even my low-cost expenses could not be covered. As matters stood, it was hard to find 13 Belizean-born players for a squad, when the speck of a nation then had a population of only 120,000. It did have eight semi-professional football clubs (that grew to 12 over time). Still, the World Cup qualifiers were a lot of fun and we played many international friendlies. We never won a game but under my tutelage, our conceding of goals dropped dramatically. During my three-year tenure, I took the squad to Panama, Costa Rica, Guatemala, Honduras and Nicaragua, among others. And when the Belize national police team played in the various

Caribbean police confederation cups, I got to see even more places with them. Barry Bowen, a local businessman, kindly assumed all the costs.

Last, but not least, I undertook kidnap and ransom (K&R) negotiation assignments for a London-based company, operated and mostly staffed by former SIS intelligence officers. I brought with me my vast experience in analyses of political affairs while working as an NOC in varied foreign locations. So, I got to learn the ins and outs of hostage negotiation as I went along the pipeline, learning on the job. While not exactly halfway between Mexico and Venezuela, the two most notorious kidnapping countries in the world, to British eyes Belize was more or less considered halfway. Factually, as the crow flies from where I lived on Ambergris Caye, the Mexican border was only 20 miles away across the water. You could see it from the north end of the island. Cancun was a half-day bus ride up the coast from the Corozal-Chetumal border post. If I couldn't fly out of Belize City to wherever I had to go to, then the airport at Cancun was the alternate gateway to the bigger, wider world out there.

We typically worked in three-man multi-lingual teams. I could have been employed full-time had I chosen to be, as there were too many innocent people (called 'the taken') being grabbed from all over the region and held for ransom. But I accepted K&R assignments only after the football season had ended. There were sound reasons for not taking a full-time job, despite the excellent pay. For one, K&R is a pressure-cooker type of environment so the burnout rate was high. The setting was incredibly stressful. We were regularly dealing with life and death situations, including safeguarding our own lives. But I felt I was doing some good for people that didn't deserve to be taken away from their loved ones. In all this, I was reminded that my best friend at SIS, Dave Brennan, had given his all in Central America to see justice upheld. More than anything else, he was the motivator for why I stayed in this line of work for so long. The plus side was I got to see not only Mexico and Venezuela a lot, but also Guatemala and Honduras. Colombia and Paraguay featured frequently on the schedule as well. And it was around this time I first heard on our intercom on one particular job, "We have a code amber situation." It meant, 'I've gone to take a pee, back in a minute.' So even the world of K&R has its own lingo – some light relief exists in a dark place!

At times, what the stealers (called 'the takers') and their henchmen could be capable of doing was chilling. They invariably came from the class of hardened criminals looking to fatten their wallets at the expense of everything else. Others were revolutionaries seeking to fund their wars. Occasionally, right-wing militias entered the fray as well. Their activities supported death squads needing money to pay off the assassins of lefties, who had themselves robbed wealthy right-wingers. Producers of horror movies and their screenwriters could have hardly imagined more ghastly scenarios of twitching curtains and screams.

It is often claimed that psychopaths are not mentally insane. They know full well what they are doing, and when they don't get their way, they can exhibit depraved reactions. They lack remorse and feel absolutely no empathy for their victims. To them, the hapless individuals are regarded as nothing more than commodities or bargaining chips. In essence, they are like robots functioning inside a human body. It is the best way to depict the mentality of these craven criminals. To describe them as anything but zombie-like creatures, would be overly kind.

Many of them were high octane on cocaine most of the time. And they had no fear of the consequences of their actions, on themselves or on others. A commonly used terminology in K&R operations was to refer to persons under the influence of cocaine as resultant blue. Conversely, the non-resultant blue meant that the suspect tested negative for cocaine. The origin of the colour terms came from the field drug-testing kits we routinely and randomly used to check for the presence of illegal narcotics on suspects and related finds. A sample containing traces of coke would turn blue in seconds. Hence the use of the colour as a descriptive term. Similarly, a sample containing marijuana would become purple and one containing heroin would change its colour to green.

The amount of impure cocaine on the market was shocking. Of course, an overdose of pure coke could kill a user in hours. Contaminated white stuff invariably led to similar tragic consequences for the unsuspecting drug user. Narcotics circulating on the black market were often spiked with ingredients used in the production of cement, or powders derived from dried battery acid. These ruses were intended to trick the addict into thinking he was getting his daily dose at a great discount. Nothing was further from the truth. These tainted fake drugs invariably condemned the aficionada to a slow and painful death.

I'd seen my share of evil acts in my intel career, while operating on the frontline in warzones. But I didn't think Man was capable of inflicting some of the unnecessary cruelty I saw in Central America. In one gory instance, a European woman had her finger cut off with a machete simply because she couldn't get her wedding ring off fast enough for the kidnappers, who were known as *secuestradores* in the local lingo. This was the level of depravity we were dealing with each and every time. The combined impact of the unrelenting violence was difficult to bear. I confess that with so many such cases to deal with, the whole situation evolved into a constant blur. One case came right after another. It was never ending. And despite our best efforts, the success rate was no better than 50%. This meant that in half the cases, we failed to secure the release of the kidnapped and save their lives. Many victims were never traced and remain unaccounted for. In a perverse way the police in Mexico often recorded such cases as 'throat-splits', as if this explained how the case ended.

A key factor in dealing with the extortionists is that you have to think like them in order to prevail over them. One way to enter their brain's mechanism is to imagine the worst nightmare you have ever had and then let it play out as though it was real life. This being a fact, even though escapism gets a bad name in psychology for the simple reason it involves avoiding realism. Only then could one begin to understand how crazy it was out there. And this coming from a person who doesn't remember dreams at all, yet saw plenty of lurid acts of unspeakable horrors materialise right in front of my eyes.

You've got to get past the emotional armour violent kidnappers put up.

Those of us who found ourselves in this kind of environment tried to make sense of the realities the best way we could. Most of us usually failed to fully accept our lot. Many of the K&R guys, flush with being paid in tax-free cash, got drunk after a job was over. I refused to succumb to the proverbial slippery slope and managed to remain sober even at the worst of times. *Once the booze is in, the wits are out* was a saying. In some way, I realised that I was a fairly well-to-do British person living among a Spanish-speaking populace filled with destitution, and fuelled by rage at the excesses of the few rich people living among them. I, too, could mistakenly have switched places and become a victim. While not precisely teetotal, I would restrict myself to just the one beer at all times.

Though I understood the fury, I could never accept the violence directed at innocent children, not old enough to have been guilty of anything yet. I fully accepted that the mind-sets of the bad boys were polar opposite to mine. Maybe in the heads of these thugs, the rich kids' lives counted for nothing, in the race to collect more moolah to spend. In this respect, there is *a long overdue need to address the growing gap that separates the rich from the poor.*

One effective way helped me cope with the angst I experienced during intense times. I recalled reading about the American psychiatrist, Stanley Milgram. In the 60s, he opined that in the agentic state an individual defines himself as an instrument carrying out the wishes of others. Essentially, he was saying that people yield to those perceived to be in authority, and in doing so become detached from their own actions. In short, they would evolve into automatons, slavishly obeying the commands of the masterminds in charge of them. So my original robot analogy wasn't far off the mark. The free drugs the kidnappers had available to them provided an added incentive and motivation, I suppose. Ironically, the United States is not the only country where the people claim an inherent right to own guns. Guatemalans and Mexicans share this credo as well. It is difficult to overstate the abundance of dangerous weapons being carried around in these two places.

A very acute problem that Mexico faced in particular related to the entrenched corruption of politicians, police chiefs and army commanders. Many of them became enablers and protectors of criminals. By working with the crime syndicates, they shared in the profits derived from the illegal trade. *Those elected officials who were sworn-in to protect the people and enforce the rule of law were the enemy within.*

Fortunately, very early into this game, I inadvertently created my own luck to weasel through this jigsaw of a puzzle. One day while in Belize, I happened to read an unusual plea on the fledging internet, which few had access to. At the time, the net was still in its infancy and service was delivered by radio from the capital, Belize City. It could be sporadic at times, just like the electricity was. According to this specific blog, a young woman living in the States had been legally adopted as a baby in Belize by a white family from the US. Now in her teens, she was desperate to locate her Mayan blood relatives. She was born in Belize, and had the blessing of her American parents to find her biologic parents and siblings. Her memory of her older brother fitted one of the footballers in my island-based squad, amazingly. He'd had a big toe missing from birth (on his main kicking foot, the lad being a left winger). She couldn't have possibly remembered this detail on her own, since she was a baby when she was adopted, so perhaps the American man and his wife recalled this unusual fact.

It was the off-season at the time, so I biked over to where my player lived with his married sister. The woman answered the door holding her own baby in her arms. She said her brother was away in Mexico for several months. After I told her why I was there, she fainted right there and then in front of me. I barely managed to just catch the wee toddler before the mother tumbled to the floor.

When she finally regained her composure, she admitted that she and her brother had often wondered about their younger sister and her fate. She said that their parents had passed away ruing their decision to give their third child up for adoption. They had to because of their inability to feed the baby. The long and short of this story is that upon the return of the brother from Mexico, they used my house phone to call their sister in the States and re-established the long-severed connection. Within a few months they were all happily reunited when the younger sister arrived on the island with the American couple in tow. I was invited to the gathering but, regretfully, I was abroad on another K&R missing person op. I was sad I missed the party but later on I saw all the joyous photographs taken at the celebration. It's a good feeling to contribute to unbridled happiness.

This story did not end there, however. It turned out that the Belizean laddie of Mayan descent, wanted to repay me for my good deed, and he did so. He was an equable character who played in the town football squad and never got in trouble with the refs for dissent or fouls. Once he figured out the reason for my frequent and long absences from Ambergris Caye, he requested I come with him via Guatemala into the mountains of Mexico. He said he wanted me to meet the person he worked for in the off-season. It took us ten full days of travel involving slow bus rides and walking treks to reach our destination. I then got to meet the outlawed, revolutionary, leftist Zapatista Army of National Liberation (*Ejército Zapatista de Liberación*

Nacional or EZLN), in the mountainous region of Chiapas. The rebels were led by a former teacher who called himself Sub-Commander Marcos. A pipe-smoking, balaclava-wearing man, he had fought for indigenous people's rights since a 1994 rebellion.

From the get-go, the sub-commander and I got along very well. In fact, he encouraged me to call him Rafa in private, when he removed his ski mask. I explained to Rafa the problems I occasionally experienced while carrying out my K&R duties. In many instances I encountered corrupt Mexican officials, who happened to also be his adversaries. The crux of the matter was that I was given an invaluable resource to lean on, whenever I ended up in a spot of bother in Mexico. When I felt I needed assistance, I could rely on the local members of the outlawed Zapatista rebels to cover my back. Marcos gave me a code word to utter to the manager of any bus station in the region, who would then put me in touch with a contact of the Zapatista Army. I would have a second confirmation phrase ready to verbalise in order to present my credentials, and the answer had to be correct as well. Every time the introduction system was changed, my footballer's family, or the lad himself, delivered me the new one in Belize. This procedure of absolute trust gave me the confidence to switch gears whenever I was confronted with examples of outrageous sleaze in K&R ops. I'm pleased to say that many innocent lives were indeed spared thanks to the Rafa/Marcos connection.

And Rafa explained to me how the EZLN never succumbed to making profits from illegal activities like cocaine and human trafficking. Instead, amazingly, several well-known American rock bands who sympathised with his movement donated royalties and gig monies to his cause via US-based non-profits. I knew of a couple of famous British acts (from my vinyl record pressing days) that were also in a position to do the same. Admirably, the end result was these groups also regularly contributed funds to EZLN, also through legal UK charities.

Prior to our departure from the EZLN's jungle headquarters (we took a different route on our return trip to Belize) I presented the football-loving Marcos/Rafa with a farewell gift. It was my blue and black striped jersey of Internazionale Milan football club. In our time talking together he expressed his admiration for the Italian club's lone star above its logo, which is because they were the European Cup holders once. The icon and the name reminded him of The Internationale (the world socialist anthem), a song he knew by heart. He was, of course, delighted to receive the used shirt from me. For my part it was only a small token of my gratitude for helping me in my K&R work.

* * * * * * * * *

The world of K&R is, what someone once described as, penumbral…meaning that often the solution to the problem lies in the shaded area of a shadow. As a thinking man, I thought that the analogy was quite appropriate. The difference between success and failure could hinge on where the dark colours gradually faded and merged with another dark colour. *But I took that to also mean the search inside the soul of a person.* Surely you could appeal to certain bad boys and plead for mercy on behalf of the person they held. Not every kidnapper was bad, only most of them were. Nothing personal, mind you, it was just how they were conditioned to survive. Despite the long odds, my requests for clemency worked sometimes, especially where children were involved.

Certainly, no two jobs were similar. Each unfolded in its own unique way and at its own speed. Sometimes I was the designated number three of a trio, while at other times I took the second-in-charge spot. As time went by, and my Spanish improved, I eventually became the honcho heading up a three-man team. The most often used words out in the field were: *todo cambia* (everything changes), *paciencia* (patience), *cojones* (show backbone) and *camarón* (shrimp). The latter term referred to the size of a male genitalia, and wasn't something to eat.

Then there was the toxic mix of vicious macho gangs *(pandillas)*, the open use of switchblades, the senseless overconsumption of beer, the slums that lacked electricity and running water, the overpowering stench, the local unlimited availability of drugs, the wide-spread trafficking of illegal narcotics, and the virtual absence of legitimate employment opportunities. Instead, people worked for buttons when a job was found or went for part-time vocations to bring bread home. To put food on the table, men took to bootlegging, and women did tricks in knocking shops – which is British security slang for brothels.

The crushing effect of poverty weighed heavily on the masses. For them it was like life was going in endless circles. So, you can see how and why this cesspool had sucked everybody down into an underworld that was very visible even at the surface. Not just in Belize, where I called home at the time, but all over Central and South America this exploitation of the desperate seemed to have taken permanent hold. It was certainly a sight for sore eyes. Some called it *La Garra* or The Claw, as in a mouse held by the claws of a cat. And this was just at the bottom end of the pecking order mess that got uglier as you climbed the ladder.

In sharp contrast, nearby gleaming holiday resorts were false centres of cool springing up everywhere. Cash-rich foreign tourists were flashing their wealth in an obscene manner. Places like Cancun were not at all representative of Mexico, but rather depicted some kind of vacant plastic replicas ripped out of a fold-out glamour magazine, including the fake palm trees. An eyesore of a different kind to those that had moved from living inside cardboard boxes to tin huts. The social order was lop-sided, but rather than climb the ladder to success the slow way, some of the impoverished chose the faster criminal track of easier pickings to try and reach the top. As a result, many suffered dire consequences and paid for their poor choices with their own lives and the lives of fallen others.

* * * * * * * * *

As a prelude to K&R negotiations, initial contact was nearly always established by the takers. They naturally wanted a reward in exchange for the kidnapped, so that was a given. The hideouts they chose were invariably at locations that were familiar to them. We took for granted that everybody and his mother around us could be working in league with them. As a result, we trod cautiously but stayed wired to all kinds of possibilities unravelling, and then some. Paradoxically, while the kidnappers were eager to receive their pay-out, some of them were recalcitrant and often engaged in passive non-compliance, time wasting, as they tried to throw us off their scent.

Whenever I was in charge of negotiations, I had to behave like a man who has been there before and had seen it all. I had to project the persona of someone who knew exactly where to go, without hesitation, even though I hadn't been within a hundred or even a thousand miles of the stinking hell-hole. Understand please, these events took place before the days of trackable mobile phones and the internet being available to all and sundry.

The way someone finding themselves in this position talks, sends an unmistakable signal that is clearly picked up by the other party. It is very much about controlling your adversaries to think and behave in the manner you want them to. The methods we employed have their roots in SIS (MI6) psychogramming (psychology combined with programming) and are aimed to draw out answers and to subtly dominate the subject of conversation. Understandably, the first objective is to obtain proof of life (Polaroid photo with the day's newspaper is best) or footprints in life (confirming use of credit card or phone call received) from these bastards of the person(s) they were holding against their will. Otherwise, announcing our presence and disclosing our location would have all been in vain.

If they hadn't already thought how to prove that fact, it told me they were inexperienced novices or had other motives. The weather-beaten old hands at this brutal game had their proof at the ready. Windows of opportunity (called WOO) are limited and time is of the essence. The reason was they didn't want to string out the negotiations for too long. They just wanted to get their hands on the US dollars, paid in a swap for who they were holding, and then move on, pronto. Otherwise they'd murder the victim. Then they would just go and find another target to hijack. It was all in a normal day's work.

After proof of life or footprints in life were secured, the next goal was to set achievable objectives. *With progress comes breathing space.* I did not expect us to agree on everything but a must was to compromise on preconditions – give a little to get a little back.

One method that worked well most of the time was a take on a children's game. I'd deliver a message to the kidnappers to furnish five of their demands in writing. Then I'd get the note delivered in a sealed envelope to a designated dead letter box that Americans call dead drop. And while they were there my own envelope with my five demands was already in place, ready to be switched.

Frequently we used a more dynamic method of exchange. We would drive a car in the outside lane towards a designated traffic light at night time, with all the windows down, and one of us holding the envelope out of the window. A two-man motorbike with lights off and without licence plates, would approach our vehicle from behind and pull alongside (or it could be going in the opposite direction and come from in front). The helmeted rider of the bike would usually snatch the envelope from the outstretched hand. Simultaneously, the passenger also wearing a helmet on the back of the motorbike would toss their envelope, or notepaper elastic-banded around a stone, onto the back seat of our vehicle. With the exchange completed, the motorbike would then accelerate into the dark. The times we carried this exchange off could be between X and Y hours. Sometimes we were forced to fill as much as three hours in idle wait. The mechanics of the exchange were dictated by them. Always at their discretion, not ours. Naturally, we were armed to protect ourselves in case of a change in their plans. Every once in a blue moon that stone became a brick through the window, minus any message attached to it, making *that* the memo they were sending. Usually that signalled the deal was off. And the resultant body wasn't always found afterwards.

If any of our respective demands matched then it would be instantly agreed to, obviously. The very fact we were in agreement on one issue established a bond of sorts. Failing this then we each had up to ten other avenues to consider. At least it was a start in communications.

The main objective from our side of the fence was to establish whether the taken persons were still alive. The takers had to show 'n' tell by any credible means they chose. The main objective from their side of the fence was to establish whether the monies were realistically forthcoming and when they would likely be delivered. The latter task required the cooperation of families, employers, insurance companies and banks. It was not always easy to coordinate, when time was of the essence. On rare occasions, I actually carried $50,000-$60,000 in large denomination unmarked bills in my bags. In such instances, the objective was to effect a quick deal for a lower amount, instead of waiting for the bigger pot to arrive. It worked only half the time though.

In a hostage negotiation, unpredictable events and unintended consequences can complicate matters and hinder progress towards a successful resolution. You have to be unprejudiced. It's the consistency in your team's vocal and written delivery that smooths a poor situation over and improves the chances for a fruitful exchange. Even humour works sometimes. Some of them said they even liked dealing with an Englishman who was far removed from his homeland. Because I had a moustache and long dark hair then, I had inherited the street name of El Mosquetero (The Musketeer), which I kind of liked. At least they remembered me! But any erratic behaviour rocks the boat. Resolving the problem through good faith, while keeping everybody at the table and being sincere, are the key traits of an effective negotiator. Like anything else, you are walking a fine line as you've got to make the takers see the unreality of their demands. This is especially true if the ransom demand is too high or even non-achievable. At this point you attempt to reason with them that committing violence won't work. In rare circumstances, you would ask them to reconsider their demands and avoid unnecessary bloodshed. At the same time, you would also offer them a way out without embarrassing themselves, i.e. give up their ransom demands and release the victim unharmed or take the option of a smaller payment. But, as already stated, the success rate of such negotiations was no better than even odds.

* * * * * * * * *

Obviously, I have amassed a thick dossier of tales about my involvement in these kinds of operations. In fact, I may have material to someday fill a full-length book on the subject. But for now, a couple of examples will suffice. Both cases illustrate the two extremes of the spectrum. They are rather unusual in their telling:

One sunny morning in 1997, I received a phone call from the company that hired me regularly for K&R assignments. "Would I be interested in spending a couple of nights in next door Honduras with some filmmakers' seeking possible shooting locations for an upcoming motion picture?" asked the voice from London.

I had nothing going on then, so I accepted the assignment. To save time, I took the 20-minute puddle-jump in a Tropic Air small prop plane across to Belize City's International Airport. There I boarded a TACA, the acronym for *Transportes Aereos del Continente Americano*, Boeing 737 flying from Miami on its way to its hub of San Salvador, the capital of El

Salvador. The jet had another scheduled stopover en route, in the Honduran town of San Pedro Sula – my intended destination. It wasn't until the aircraft was coming down to land that I remembered that San Pedro Sula, at the time, had the highest murder rate in the world!

In the crowded arrival area, I was met by two well-dressed tall white men, a Brit and an American. They stood out like beanpoles in a sea of smaller, thinner and darker Centro Americanos. After shaking hands, we headed out to their jeep, which was driven by an amiable local Honduran man. We fist greeted each other, in the local way. He never told me his name but there was a machine gun lying between the seats that announced his credentials. I asked him if he had a spare pistol. Without a word he removed a loaded piece from the glove compartment and presented it to me with the barrel facing the floor. The other two sat in the back, seemingly oblivious to the danger around them. Soon we were out in the countryside with a tape recorder on, as they asked me questions about K&R. At the same time, they kept their eyes skinned for possible location shoots while the two of us in the front had one eye out for armed bandits instead.

They were in the production team for a proposed big-budget movie to be titled *Proof of Life*. The lead roles were yet to be cast but the above- and below-the-line financial plan was already set. The former represents the fees the actors and actresses would get while the latter reflected the crew's salaries and other filming costs. Several stars were said to be interested in appearing in the would-be feature film. However, they were withholding their acceptance pending their approval of the final screenplay. It was why the two co-producers were talking to me. They were hoping to make the scenes as realistic as possible by picking the brain of someone who had 'done all that'. I should also mention the remuneration already paid to London for my time and services was substantial, plus my return airfare, food and accommodation. I was only too happy to provide my insights, while thinking I could buy some much-needed football gear for the guys back in Belize.

So I did what I was paid to do. I answered their questions for 48 hours, and then offered some other suggestions they could potentially shoot (excuse the pun). At one point, I said that gestures of goodwill worked well in the field. Trades and exchanges between the negotiating parties for this and that. The main observation was that almost all the kidnapped individuals who were rescued from their captivity in the wildernesses, had long filthy fingernails. As recounted by them, they needed those fingernails to dig up the soil to unearth slugs and other edible insects. Some long-term captives were allowed to grow mini-gardens by their captors. Most of the newly freed were close to starvation and, of course, emaciated – with dirty lengthy and straggly hair. Many would weep with joy, too, at their escape from bondage, and we would cry also. It was almost always emotional to witness. The best I ever heard was one man screaming how happy he was to come back to life again! That was a really good feeling.

With the consultation job done, I flew back by TACA to Belize and home, never to give this time away a second thought. A real kidnapping had taken place in Paraguay so I was soon taking off down to Asunción, its capital.

Six years later I was in England visiting a British friend of mine in Worthing, West Sussex. We passed the local cinema and I stopped in my tracks when I saw the poster for *Proof of Life,* a new movie release starring Russell Crowe and Meg Ryan. The afternoon showing was about to start so we paid and headed in to watch the film.

I must say the producers did a good job of it. It was a big studio-made feature, shot on location in more peaceable Ecuador, and not risky Honduras. The hostage negotiator Crowe was playing, was an Englishman and a veteran of the Special Air Service (SAS)! I'm sure many of the ex-SIS fellows in London were not happy with the switch, but maybe the filmmakers thought it was sexier. Ryan was the American wife of the kidnapped person. The screenwriters had evidently included numerous details I had mentioned to the co-producers way back then. Amazingly, the movie included the part about the rescued party's having long dirty fingernails and how they would cry with happiness at being freed!

There was one big point the filmmakers got wrong though. I don't recall them asking me anything related to it anyway. It is well known that due to established policies of certain governments, the insurance companies and corporations in those countries have a 'non-policy' clause in their insurance terms. It means that they will not pay ransoms under any circumstances, because complying with the takers' demands would only encourage more acts of kidnapping. To their cold minds it adds fuel to the fire and the vicious circle would keep going around. The US, UK and Israel are among those known for refusing to pay ransoms at all for the safe return of their citizens. They routinely, flat out, won't even consider such a move. In the movie the taken person was an American executive. At least in this instance, Hollywood must have consciously decided to include factual inaccuracies in the story for the sake of dramatic effects.

Overall, I was quite chuffed about how the story unfolded on the silver screen. It's just a pity that smells cannot be incorporated into films to better convey reality.

(The other extreme of K&R follows in the next chapter, the real hands-on version.)

* * * * * * * * *

Chapter Six

Hate. Fate. Destiny. Buzz. Control. Lust. Greed. Payback.
You never know how someone's mind works.
What their intentions are.
The brutal truth is
...unknown

The 'Jungle Hub for World Outlaws', is a fitting name once coined by a knowledgeable and well-connected journalist for Ciudad del Este (City of the East), Paraguay's second largest metropolis. This place of 300,000 inhabitants, lies 300 km (about 186 miles) due east by highway from the capital of Asunción, where I had flown into. It sits strategically right at the junction where Argentina, Brazil and Paraguay meet. The post-midnight drive in the dark took exactly three hours and we reached our destination at 3 AM. I remember thinking everything has the number 3 in it. Our car's licence plate even had several 3's in it. Was it a premonition?

Its name had been changed in 1989 from Puerto Flor de Lis (Port Lily Flower), but it's hard to imagine how the city merited its original name, which conjures a thing of beauty. The reality is far different. It is an overcrowded web of ugly dwellings and a haven for smugglers. Anything illegal and illicit is carried out in broad daylight. All around, unpleasant smells and noxious fumes fill the air. The often-crawling road traffic meanders through the town centre in all directions producing an insane haze along the way. The city is also, surprisingly, a maze where supporters of Islamic extremism teem brazenly in their hundreds, as many of the street merchants are of Arabic descent. A portion of their profits, it was rumoured, was being sent to fund the crazed terrorist activities of Hezbollah (Party of God), half way around the world in the Middle East. Nobody present in South America's humid centre of sleaze was in the slightest fazed by the most recent sobriquet. Perhaps a more descriptive name for this municipality in the middle of Latin America would have been the City of Beasts.

Like always, when first arriving in slimy sweaty shitholes full of fiendish cocksuckers and motherfuckers, I felt the tension rise within myself. A feeling of being in the eye of the storm: quiet and windless on the inside of a cocoon while a maddening tempest rages on the outside.

On top of this, the client we'd come to see wasn't ready to see us just yet. So on my first evening there, I decided to lay myself bare to all and sundry by taking a banya. It is similar to a sauna session except the assistant assails your body and legs with a kind of bush stick that purportedly opens and cleans the pores in your body. Thereafter you plunge into cold water, supposedly to close the skin's apertures. Well it was quite an experience, I must say! Interestingly, I had heard of the term banya before, in Russia as well as in Muslim nations. It could even be derived from Spanish, though I'm not exactly sure where the word comes from. It is, nevertheless, widely used. I might also add that I was offered the services of a teenage hooker that came gratis with the fee, but I respectfully declined the offer. Moreover, my offbeat humour told me it would have been an irony getting a sexually transmitted disease while in the process of giving the body a thorough cleansing. Walking back on the humid poorly-lit streets, I could hear the vermin scuttling about in the open sewers. It made me shiver and feel dirty again.

The exercise did clear the recent stress that had built up in me, I'll give it credit for that. The flight down from Belize City via Miami had been arduous to say the least. My journey included three long stopovers en route as a direct flight was not available. After Florida, too many immigration and custom officials in Caracas, and then some more uniforms in Buenos Aires, showed deep interest in the small box of tricks I had packed in my cabin carry-on – my only luggage. They were especially curious to understand what the small panoramic detection mirror on a retractable stick did. It was a tool used for observation around corners. Thank goodness, the swivel joint for accurate scoping and adjustment of angles was not inspected. Similarly, they examined the mini telescope, suspecting it had a secret firing compartment inside it. It didn't. They were equally keen to keep pressing my mechanically-operated torch (flashlight). They were simply fascinated such a device could work indefinitely without ever needing batteries. I needed these essential tools of the trade for my upcoming assignment and I didn't need any of them being confiscated. At the end of a long day of faffing around they weren't. It wasn't everyday they saw a British passport holder pass through their neck-of-the-woods, I suppose, even though one of them volunteered that eight million Americans have concealed weapons permits, as if that was a good reason for detaining me…

The following morning, I was fully rested and ready to face the cruel world again, as were the other two hombres assigned to my team. Upon landing at Asunción airport, I'd immediately spotted the men in the arrival hall. One of them was a 6'8" Argentine national and former special-forces soldier, with long hair, who played rugby in his spare time. He went by the name of Ricardo. He smiled a lot and was generally a happy-go-lucky type of guy. The third member, called DPF, was a chain-smoking, unsmiling and slightly overweight ex-Paraguayan policeman half the size and width of Ricardo, who had not much hair left on his head. I have no idea what his monogram stood for, and I never enquired. When DPF was out of earshot once I remember a grinning Ricardo figuring it stood for Da Paraguayan Fucker. Gave me a belly laugh!

And to them I never used my real name. They called me The Musketeer, or *El Mosquetero*, as I was widely known in the kidnap and ransom (K&R) business by now. I had worked with each of them before but this was the first time we operated together as a trio. Neither were stuntmen-types, being more methodical in their work ethic. Both were dependable chaps, responsible, with young families, and for whom moderation was always an option – so not prone to being intimidated by any crazy dude. We all were authorised to trade, a K&R industry word meaning to negotiate, at our own discretion and as we saw fit. However, our dealings had to be within the framework of the rest of the team. In my global travels I have always enjoyed the occasional back-to-front imperfect language of the way many foreigners spoke English, finding it rather quixotic. These two chaps were no different. How they structured their syntax was not important to me as long as I could understand them. The main point, however, was for us to watch and protect each other's back. That's all we cared about…but it came second after the first objective of freeing the victims was accomplished.

The background folder we'd each received was overnighted from London before we left our respective departure points. The gist of it was: a wealthy cattle rancher, who had turned half his sprawling *finca* (farm) into a thriving soy bean producing enterprise, had had his eight-year daughter abducted on her way to school three days ago. Her two male *guardaespaldas* (bodyguards) in the ensuing raging gun battle had perished in the bullet-ridden car during the ambush. Within hours, according to the local police, the takers made their demands known by directly calling the Paraguayan self-made multi-millionaire on a phone equipped with an untraceable voice encoder. For the safe return of the girl, the kidnappers wanted a sum of US$750,000 in cash, expressly stipulating that no tracing dyes were to be used. They also made the unusual step of selecting this misnomer of a squalor of civilisation as the site for the exchange. It was probably their own backyard, where they were safe among other thieves. Hence, the reason we were here on the rancher's behalf, as ordered in by Lloyds of London who held his family insurance policy, via our employer, who was also based in Britain's capital city. You have to appreciate that for obvious reasons a large majority of such cases are never reported in the news, like this one wasn't.

* * * * * * * * *

(I am attempting to explain what goes on in the field of K&R. Many factors come into play. Some are considered initially relevant, others become irrelevant over time. Scenarios can get fudged as supposed clues are intentionally designed to mislead trackers. There is a jumble of information thrown at us. Often confusion reigns, but good operators eventually see their way through. This job threw the bus at us hunter-gatherer types from a number of angles, but our perseverance steered a way around the barriers.)

Now that we were all onsite, we had to connect the dots. Setting off in our mid-size rent-a-car, which we'd collected at the airport, our first port of call was the millionaire's rancho. We had to pass through the layers of unfriendly *autodefensa*, the rancher's private army surrounding his property. Seemed to me the man definitely had enemies, considering how many of them were present to protect the property. Each face skittish, unfriendly, armed, muscular and ready. Not surprising considering what had happened 72 hours prior. We were all gruffly ordered out of the vehicle, patted down, while the transport's interior was searched by two big sniffer dogs – presumably one for gunpowder and the other for narcotics. "No one in their right minds messes with brute snarling power on four legs, multiplied by two," muttered Ricardo, almost to himself, as the animals' noses were switched to ourselves for a smell down.

I knew that a canine specially trained in the UK and US could detect up to nine drug odours. Fortunately, neither mutt gave indications they had detected anything of interest that would otherwise cause them to sit, then freeze like statues, in front of the scent on us. *And that was just going in.* We experienced the same rough treatment again when we left. How many other security personnel who were hidden out of sight could only be imagined.

Once inside, the huge plantation had everything one could possibly want. A large swimming pool – half covered indoors and half outdoors with diving boards. Stables for many horses, three armour-plated limos (the weight on the wheels gave them away), and original paintings of well-known contemporary artists adorning the walls. I lost count of how many rooms were part of the main residence. Each had its own immaculate décor and colour-coordinated theme. You couldn't help but notice a lot of staff were in attendance. Clearly the family were loaded and they flaunted moolah in their own unique way.

The missing kid was their only child. The photographs furnished to us showed a pretty, doll-like girl, with big eyes and silky long dark hair. She definitely possessed what I call twinkle factor. Her mum and dad were chic good lookers, and so was she. He was an older, rather brusque, hands-on guy who apparently worked around the clock. Whatever preconceived notions I had looking around this glitzy fortress, as a man, I happened to like the guy straightaway. He seemed a straightforward, humble fellow, honourable even. The wife clearly enjoyed the fruits of his labour. She was about 20 years his junior, and by all accounts a trophy wife. One couldn't help but notice she had a nice figure, inside clothes found in the boulevards of European capitals. Interestingly, she sported no jewellery. I guessed that she must have been a former beauty queen. A framed picture of her as a young attractive woman, in a swimsuit, confirmed my intuition. A sophisticated sweetie in her own right. She clearly passed her classic femininity on to her daughter. The only criticism I had of her was that the perfume she used was a bit overdone to my taste, as I stifled a sneeze.

Dealing with the stressed parents under such circumstances is awkward. So much wretched passion rides on a successful outcome. Heavy tension permeated the air, like a storm of many tears ready to rain down from the heavens. *I'd seen it before but one never gets used to witnessing the soul slowly being sapped from its core.* But they were holding it together as well as could be expected considering the steaming pile of shit they were having to deal with. They sat there with their arms around each other, both sniffling from time to time. Both of them spoke English well. Unprompted, he recounted that when he was a single man he had travelled far and wide. He said he had been to my homeland of England, and had lived in Switzerland for a full year. He then duly demonstrated his multi-lingual skills with a select few sentences in French, German and Italian, all the while holding my eyes.

Some minutes passed before it registered with me why he lapsed into languages nobody present but me understood. I nodded briefly at him supportively, while my team mates exchanged discomfited glances with each other because they didn't know what he was prattling on about. It turned out during our mostly stilted brief discussion that he was the step-father and not the biologic father. Both had been married before. He was a widower while she was a divorcee. Between the two of them they had produced just the one offspring that was now missing.

I had an acute sense that a member of their large workforce could have been involved with the bad boys. In fact, some of the workers lived in the servants' quarters. A possible snitch within. In K&R it was called internal conspiracy (inside job). But we didn't have the time to grill them all. The route to the school and their approximate time of departure seemed to have been widely known on the day of the snatch. My suspicion was confirmed when the map we found in the room of one of the dead live-in bodyguards was well-marked with a fluorescent pink pen, along with four alternate routes to the seminary. Several receipts of purchased petrol on the same table told a story of which fill-up station was their most favoured. They both died for their dumb-ass folly by advertising their pattern of life (daily activities).

On the way back from the villa we stopped at the crime scene, or rather at the site where the attack took place. The only clues that anything had happened at this kill zone three days prior, were the skid marks burned into the asphalt's surface. Evidently, the car had to brake hard, before it was forced off the road. It ended up being wrapped around the only tree in plain sight for hundreds of metres. We could see where the bark had been stripped off from the tree upon impact. There was still a faint waft of a chemical pervading the air. Perhaps the maintenance crew had used a strong scouring agent of some sort. I supposed the local council's various blue light emergency response workers had efficiently scrubbed off everything else.

Despite all our concerted effort, we couldn't get a handle on where the incoming shots had been fired from. I got to think the killers used a long-range high-powered rifle. From that moment onwards, I had a sixth sense that we were in the viewfinder of someone watching over us from a distance. All the bullet casings, glass and debris had already been cleared by the police. At least we didn't find any. Even the blood that was presumably shed had been spotlessly washed away by the ambulance paramedics or fire brigade clean-up team.

While performing this forensic inspection, DPF received a call from the local police on his satellite phone, which had its own special carrying case. The news passed on by DPF left us speechless and opened our collective set of eyes wide. We got to learn that the bodies of the two deceased men had been neatly arranged alongside each other outside the car to form crucifix positions. Each cadaver had a blown-up natural colour condom stuck in its mouth. What was the significance of this shocking spectacle and what message was it meant to convey? It was a very strange way of communication under any circumstance. It signalled a carefully planned execution rather than the more common robbery-type waylay. It told me the firing party was not present at the scene. Another bunch must have carried out this bizarre arrangement in the immediate aftermath of the killings. Mucho money was behind this in order to pay the gang of support villains.

The ambush occurred on a wide-open straight stretch of road, dissecting a fairly flat countryside. Saplings, called *quebracho* by the locals, rose every few hundred metres on both sides of the road. DPF had mentioned that the name of the tree was derived from 'axe breaker', as the wood was exceptionally hard. Some dwellings stood in the distance. We walked over to several of them but there was nothing doing. The only responses we got were repeated shrugs from the peasants, the *campesinos*, living there. With downcast eyes, they collectively, understandably, claimed ignorance. Something like this was out of their league, obviously. They had heard and seen nothing, even though the violent incident took place in broad daylight and in plain sight from their doorsteps. This reluctance to talk was typical. Potential witnesses refused to get involved or didn't want to know. Irrespective of what native language you spoke in, you had to avoid a confrontational tone and instead adopt a soft and measured demeanour. I had even gone through the various sounds of what a gun sounds like with the godly head villager in a vain attempt to extract some useful intel from him. For example, a Kalishnikov sounds like 'chuh, chuh, chuh', others like 'ppp, ppp' and a loud one-time 'splt'. But he replied he was hard-of-hearing, all the while making the sign of the cross after each utterance he made.

The bells were ringing (an intel phrase for near total certainty). This strike (raid) was no low-signature hit. I got to thinking back to my time in the SIS as a croppy (covert reconnaissance operative) when truth isn't whether an event happened or not, but whether it can be substantiated. The problem is that government security agencies employ experts who professionally make certain it can't be proven, full-stop.

We went to have lunch in a dingy roadside eatery that the local transport industry frequented. Based on the stares directed at us, we were evidently the best dressed table in there. We discussed our initial findings between mouthfuls of the local fare. What struck us all was that we found the clues left for us to discover without looking very hard, namely at the *ranchero*. That was not the case outside the ranch where oddly enough, nothing was found at all. *Presented in black and white it was like half the eventual assessment was going to be a given but not the other half, which seemed purposefully hidden.* Usually all the initial parts to the picture we were building were jumbled up in various shades of grey. We had to sort ourselves through all the clues. Was it the takers' plan, to intentionally point us in certain directions and not others?

Case in point was at the tyre burnout scene. The placement of the cadavers in the sign of the cross and the insertion of prophylactics into their respective mouths was illogical. This gory spectacle would have rocked most hardened souls on their heels. I got to thinking that particular exercise was a deliberate attempt to distract. But from what? I had no idea. And still no visuals on the suspects by witnesses were forthcoming. Usually somebody sees something.

We did have a light-hearted moment at that motorway stop though! Ricardo being so tall, even while sitting, accidentally coughed some food and it landed below him on top of DPF's head as he was sipping his soup. The look on the smaller man's face was pure entertainment. Once he grasped what had just occurred, he exclaimed, "Fuck me, Ricardo, I can feed my own head!"

Without missing a beat, Ricardo responded with, "Yeah, but I'm breathing your smoke up here all the time, it makes me gag." We all sniggered to let out the frustration that had built up in us. Dumb stuff really. Lunchtime is laughter time.

Then we headed back to our rented cubby hole of an apartment in the city's slum area to await further contact. The accommodation had been reserved by London in a filthy, rat-infested neighbourhood without any consideration for our personal comfort. We supposed that was done for a reason. DPF then went off to buy some provisions at one of the nearby *bodegas*, small stores that stock everything in small quantities. When he returned, he said he was pretty certain he had been watched the whole time. I trusted his instincts and sent him back out again to find a bar to park himself in for an hour, and assume BOLO (Be On the Look-Out for anybody to be on the look-out for). In his new assignment, he was to act as a magnet of sorts. Buy himself a couple of beers and hang out to see who comes to him. Rather than avoid and evade I always preferred the tactic of attracting and interacting with the other side, as it moved the action along faster towards its eventual conclusion. "Whiskey, Tango, Foxtrot. WTF –

what the fuck," he smirked as he went out the door.

Anticipating is better than predicting, which is better than expecting.

Sure enough, upon his return, he told us he'd been acquainted with some of the usual winos and a couple of *paisas* (hustlers). His dry assessment was only, "Man, up in the north of South America it's snorting coke behind closed doors. But down here it's more openly smoking skunk (herbal cannabis). Through their haze they knew I wasn't from these parts because I didn't inhale, though I was getting plenty second-hand. The stink of it gets in my hair."

Well he wasn't a local since he hailed from Asunción. And he was almost bald. DPF figured the hustlers were the informant element of a bigger team, while the thugs, known as *sicarios*, who paid them would eventually make an appearance. He was on their turf after all. All part of the normal pattern being played out so far, Paraguayan-style. "I know these guys all know each other," he concluded.

While DPF was involved in sussing out the locals face-to-face, Ricardo went to see the police detective that collated the evidence from the crash scene we'd stopped at earlier in the day. Interestingly the man didn't want the big Argentine to come into the police station. So, they agreed to meet much further away in the back of a nondescript café downtown. Much like in Mexico, many of the authorities are corrupt in Paraguay. Uniformed cops don't wear their collar numbers to be easily identified. The truly good guys are aware of this reality, as well as recognising the baddies working in their midst. Such is the conundrum in the undeveloped Latino world. It is so different from the smoother-running democracies of Western Europe and North America.

For my part, I stayed indoors to hold the fort. I put my feet up and forced myself to think. And when the other two got back we pooled our thoughts once again over a few beers. *Facts can change from the last time they were reviewed.*

Naturally, after our methodical filling in of colours on the pages by numbers, we quickly built up a picture of what had happened and who were the likely perpetrators. By a process of elimination, we identified logical possibilities as we knew them to be. There was a sense of inevitability to the current macabre scenario, I must admit. All three of us separately concluded – a calculated guess really – that we were a trio of actors performing on a stage in some strange theatrical production, sponsored by shenanigans instigated at the ranch. *Not a single banana skin presented itself for us to slip on.* The kind of stage-managed information drifting our way could only have originated from someone close to the couple who knew them well. Evidently, someone was manipulating the content, with or without the knowledge of the rancher and his wife. Either/or. The hunch was too strong. Everything we came across pointed back to the *hacienda.* The estate being the centre of activity, where a paper trail was left, like it was an inside job…but who was the instigator?

An early break in the case and an important clue to the mystery came after Ricardo met the police detective a second time at a different coffee house. "The first time I met him the cop spoke in…ellipsis'…short unfinished sentences…but this time he completed them!"

Apparently, a month earlier, the ranch's bank had issued a recall on a substantial business loan due to long overdue non-payments. It was about to declare the ranch in default and to authorise the debt collectors to remove goods as collateral for the amount in arrears. The sum in question was close to a million US dollars. From the outside the entity was thriving, and we understood everybody that was employed there was fully paid up, so that didn't add up. Ricardo thought the money was being used instead to pay off a blackmailer and it had now evolved into a case of kidnapping, or made to look like one.

But DPF was of a different opinion. Why would someone who owed money kidnap their own next of kin and then murder two experienced minders as a way of delaying what was owed to the bailiffs? That part didn't make sense at this stage, unless the debtors were playing some kind of sympathy card by creating this state of affairs, which was also unlikely.

As far as I was concerned, I thought that this was one big dollop of deliberately spread '*Chinese whispers*'. I had to pause and 'translate' for my pair of Spanish-speaking amigos what that term meant. It is really a children's game whereby a story is repeatedly whispered to a sequence of players sitting in a circle. Each version of the story differs slightly from the original. But by the time the final permutation reaches the first player, it bears only a scant resemblance to the original version. Not that dissimilar to a starburst of people going in different directions. They agreed wholeheartedly with that assessment. But for what reason was this game being played? Our conclusion was simple: the masterminds of the plot were deliberately trying to confuse anybody who was attempting to figure out the jigsaw. This included us as well, *only we knew it.*

At this point Ricardo then said something strange. He reiterated what the police detective had actually said to him, "The right people don't seem scared but the wrong people are scared shitless." When prompted for elaboration by him, the plain-clothed cop simply refused to do so. He just left it hanging there. DPF questioned Ricardo whether he believed the statement. Ricardo's response was insightful. "I did at the time but come to think of it now…I feel he was planting something inside my head, wanting my eyes to look in a certain direction. Kind of giving me a clue that not all is as it seems. Like the *policía* (police) were operating with one hand behind their back and he wanted me to know that."

"In times of war, the law falls silent," muttered DPF, the ex-cop. "I didn't say that, Cicero did."

And while all this was going on, we became aware, from reading the newspapers, of the emergence of the rebel group EPP *(Ejercito del Pueblo Paraguayo)*, the Paraguayan People Army. Apparently, the new group had recently commenced operations. Yet nobody we'd dealt with had ever mentioned their existence. The deliberate exclusion became obvious to us. They were the armed wing of the leftist political party Patria Libre (Free Country). They had reportedly been trained in Colombia by FARC, one of Latin America's oldest insurgencies, *Fuerzas Armadas Revolucionarias de Colombia* – the Revolutionary Armed Forces of Colombia. If that were indeed the case, the Paraguayan army would have to be called in, as it would have been well beyond our remit as three of us against hundreds was a no contest.

So, which one of the possibilities on the table was it? That was the question that needed an answer. One thing was inescapable…there was a heck of a lot of money behind the perpetrators in the sense that so many people were involved in this mystery. And yet nobody wanted to identify the masterminds of this thickening plot.

Breadcrumbs dropped on trails uncover pathways that can lead to convictions. With all these uncomfortable irons in the fire, the situation warranted a closer examination. To us it appeared that whoever committed this crime wanted to get caught, or let everybody know it was them. I always believed that the cream soon rises to the top. It especially does when there is a race against the clock. Usually someone will commit a rookie mistake due to time constraints. We would have to lure them out of their shells, to expose themselves. And do it quickly. The life of a pretty little girl depended on us.

That night, soon after we turned off our lights, someone threw a Molotov cocktail under our rental car. As a result of the petrol bomb, the vehicle was destroyed. It was a complete write-off. The fire brigade came to extinguish the fire. A half-dressed DPF took the chance to chat with the firefighters' chief. Turned out his unit were the same one that responded to the incident where the kidnap took place. The fearless young fireman disclosed some eye-openers as to the current mood in his politically corrupt society. *There was a marked increase in violence all over the city and its surrounding region.* And while he desperately wanted change, he warned us he would deny ever talking to us, if asked.

To us, this was the confirmation for everything we had already discerned. Many people knew something but were living in fear of the eventual consequences…only we had yet to put our finger on who. It wasn't a good place to be for Paraguayan nationals. It was even worse for those of us who didn't belong there in the first place, like two of the three of us. And to make matters even worse, we were trapped in a fermenting dung heap like Cuidad del Este where nothing made sense.

Ricardo summed up the long, eventful, mad first day of doing business best with: "Other than the money, what is the end result, the objective that the kidnappers' want? What is the tail that wags the dog? I don't know but I want to know!"

* * * * * * * * *

To put into effect my analogy of cream rising to the top, I decided to go right to the principal of this crossword puzzle. The next day, I phoned the rancher/owner and, in French, requested him to meet me in person at his earliest convenience. I finally figured he must have, on the earlier occasion, spoken in foreign languages on purpose. I wanted a tête-à-tête, just the two of us, away from his farmstead and with no close protection in tow. I suggested the truckers stop I previously went to with Ricardo and DPF. He responded in better French than mine that he knew the place. It was midway between his little palace out in the sticks and the shitty city centre. I had asked him to dress down, so as to perhaps look like one of his soy farm workers. I also told him to look in all the corners of the eatery upon arrival. I'd be sitting alone at one of the tables wearing a black baseball cap. I advised him to be less conspicuous by driving himself in an old banger. Finally, I assured him that he would be safe while in our collective presence as I would have my two comrades, armed but incognito, at the ready should anything unexpected happen on-site. But I couldn't vouch for his road trip though. Still, in our chosen foreign language he bravely agreed to come alone, specifying a best time for himself. If his calls were recorded there was nothing we could do about it, but at least no one listening in could have passed on what our arrangements were unless he or she understood French. And as an extra precaution, I instructed him to refrain from advancing towards my spot if I had my baseball cap on backwards. In that case, he had to totally ignore me and find a place for himself somewhere else. I'd come and find him instead when I felt certain that no one was trailing him.

As dusk fell, and right on time, he ambled in at the rendezvous. From afar, he looked confident for a low-paid 'manual labourer'. I kept my cap on with the peak forward. I was pretty sure others were around to protect him. Frankly, I wouldn't have blamed him for taking those measures, given the circumstances he found himself in. Ricardo and DPF were somewhere unseen in the hall full of tables, covering my back. They blended well among the working-class Paraguayans who were engaged in mindless evening chatter, smoking, drinking and eating in the joint. The well-manicured hands and gold timepiece of the wealthy rancher betrayed his real standing. I tut-tutted to myself. Then his eye twitch revealed his inner tension, and my sympathy for him kicked in. He seemed a decent chap, not delusional in any way. He was pretty much an on-the-ball type considering the wide range of emotions he was going through. I was determined to extract from him the correct answers to my queries, whether or not I held a handgun under the table pointing at his manhood. I kept my mind quiet.

I kicked-off the meeting with a few short pleasantries while waiting for our drinks to be served. He ordered a *mosto* and I had a *tereré*, respectively sugar cane juice and herbal iced tea. My blunt opening declaration was written in English on a piece of paper, 'If you are wearing a recording device please nod at me. I don't want any evidence against you that this conversation took place.' He just stared back at me for a few seconds then shook his head sideways slowly. I wasn't sure such a legality held up in South America. But in the western world if you ask about such things, whether verbally or in writing, and they deny so and later on it is eventually used against you, then it is thrown out in a court of law as inadmissible.

So I continued. "Thank you for accepting my invitation. Perhaps you are freer to talk away from your farm. But I'm not going to blow smoke up your arse. I'm not asking you for your opinion, because the list of stuff we've come across is already broad, and not a lot of it makes any sense. I've played most of the shenanigans back like a video in my head and nothing adds up. It's like somebody is throwing many irons in the fire to make matters fiendishly more complex. The absence of alternatives makes my brain want to explode! For us, it's creating shilly-shally purposefully, which means indecisiveness. My colleagues and I interpret that someone wants to exercise total control of this situation, or wants some kind of control at its eventual conclusion. *And I have concluded that person isn't you.*

"So, sir, I want nothing but the whole truth from you, as you know it, please. If you want your step-daughter back alive and quickly, then start by saying back to me, 'I am the target of…' I will be all ears until you narrow this down and finish. You need to help us help you. We are on your side."

He began with those precise words and continued on. His eyes showed no fear. Over the half an hour we were together I learned a lot of surprising facts, which explained the multitude of oddities we'd observed so far.

Two years ago, soon after expanding his cattle business and entering into soy production, the Paraguayan government endorsed a nationwide for-profit initiative. Some of the country's most successful entrepreneurs were asked to volunteer their expertise to others that were up-and-coming. Initially he was very enthusiastic, but as time went by, he discovered that the enterprise was a front for a scam that involved embezzlement of millions of dollars and the purchase of properties with misused public funds.

"From the beginning, the appointed committee set up rules and regulations. But I found this framework was designed only for the gullible, while the privileged few had other ideas in mind. For them, it was systematic noncompliance. I found that the so-called board of advisors I was on, wilfully deviated from its responsibilities by entrusting to a single person, of questionable background, a task of national importance involving a huge amount of money.

"The ruse was simple enough. A shell company would procure land and through legal loopholes derive under-the-table cash payments and undeserved benefits. We accomplished the 'accidental' scam by first purchasing a property at inflated prices, often four times the real market value. But just before the deal went through, we demanded 'an exorbitant commission of 25% in cash, as a kind of refund with thanks'. Of course, the seller accepted the terms as he was still going to get much more than the land was worth. I was going to expose them because the practice was obviously unethical. I want to help my country develop, not shoot itself in the foot with this brazen rip-off. I want Paraguay's arrow to point the other way. This kind of artificial development causes the country to regress, rather than move forward. I'm against harming the land of my birth like this, before it even starts down the path of economic development. This kind of thing is a sure-fire, still-born move. It's also a way of laundering money.

"But, because I dissented, my wife and close members of my family are now traumatised by the chain of events that have taken place since. It started with the methodical framing of me out of spite, which I brushed aside. But now to shut me up, they've stolen my lovely baby. I cannot forgive them for this craven act."

There was more to come so I didn't say anything. He sipped his refreshment while gathering his thoughts. His hand quivered ever so slightly.

"Then the whole situation has spiralled out of control the way it has. Your car was destroyed yesterday. It sends the ultimate message to me that someone I know will be inside another car the next time around. Maybe you or me, or both of us, or your colleagues. I know full well who is behind this campaign of intimidation. But they are supported by some powerful criminal figures working in collusion with them. So to solve one hurdle I will pay the ransom demand. I already have the cash packaged, minus the tracking powder, and ready to deliver. Your specific job is to take it to them and collect my child in return. But I cannot divulge their names to you. I will take care of this my way after you leave my country. It will be done in a way the Latino machismo understands. They will be buried with their bodies' facedown!"

After he'd finished, I didn't know what to say, so I didn't. We held our eyes locked on each other for a while. The din of the hall seemed to dim then in my dome, or maybe I was overly clammy under my cap. Normally it was our role to negotiate and then arrange for the transaction to take effect. But he had done more than half of our work already. It was a condition that was once or twice removed from how we typically operated. I eventually coughed up, "Well, it *is* an unusual situation. Different to the norm. I cannot blame you for doing what you have done thus far. I will have to clear this with London first before proceeding. I will have an answer first thing in the morning. But I would feel more comfortable if you told me who 'they' are, so we know who we are dealing with. I don't like walking through doors left purposefully open without having some idea who is waiting on the other side of them. So perhaps you will disclose this information shortly? For us, it is the devil you know rather than the devil you don't know. One last query though, what was the kinky, ritualistic, thingamajig with the rubbers stuck in dead men's mouths?"

"They told me from an earlier time that would be their signature, when a push came to a shove, to know it was them."

This raised my eyebrows. That told me he had already dealt intimately with them, before the storm wreaked havoc and made the whole situation a crapshoot.

(There is a situation an ex-pilot like me knows full well and it's called 'the startle effect'. It can be defined as an uncontrollable, automatic reflex that is triggered by exposure to a sudden, intense experience that violates all conventional expectations. Everything this job was turning out to be was the *exact opposite* of that definition. So, in my mind I was accepting a phenomenon only known to myself as 'reverse startle effect'. This state of affairs was becoming unreal.)

* * * * * * * * *

*The unexpected happens so punctually
that you are saved from the bondage of plans.*

– Freya Stark

The next morning, after some hours of delay, head office gave the go ahead in writing, by transmitting a facsimile of the authorisation letter to a local hotel. While Ricardo, DPF and I were waiting for the answer to come in, we ate a full breakfast there believing we were in for a long day. Since we had last communicated with headquarters, they had upgraded this assignment to a CATEGORY 1 PRIORITY job. Regardless, because so much was out of our control, I had a strong sense of foreboding about doing things by half. Both my colleagues felt the same way. This was going to be a beast in a city of monsters, fiends and ogres.

Upon reading the fax DPF muttered sarcastically, "No element of surprise, no containment, no tactical response group, no hard entry and no positive ID to know who the ghost we are dealing with is. All we have to do is roll up, docilely hand over the bags of cash to wherever they say, then pronto, we go and collect the poor bambino. Duh. Sounds simple. No drama. We aim to serve our masters! Fuck! Our kind of rock 'n' roll show doesn't play that way!"

Ricardo chipped in, only to morosely compare this exercise to the game of building jenga blocks. You pull one block out of the bottom and put it at the top. He didn't have to say that the pile could collapse at any time.

Into the corridors of uncertainty, we tiptoed. The changeover of the human capital or ransom demand was set to begin at dusk that very same day. Seven instalments of US$100,000 per large watertight black plastic bag had been prepared in advance and stacked with used and unmarked $100 bills. Once the last delivery was effected, the whereabouts of the missing child would then be disclosed by means we didn't yet know. By nightfall we would be in a boat with no lights on going upstream on the slow-moving but wide Paraná River. (The river flows downstream to the Rio del la Plata delta over 621 miles [1,000 km] away, where the cities of Buenos Aires and Montevideo lay on the South Atlantic Ocean.) The more I learned about our upcoming task, the more a foreboding of doom and failure filled the air. It seemed to be a wing and a prayer kind of mission, and I didn't like it one bit.

The forecast had stated it would be a moonless autumn night. We could have placed a tracking device inside each of the bags but we rejected the idea because it would have been easily found when the bag was opened. I spent the remainder of the daylight hours preparing contingency plans for the three of us should things go wrong.

* * * * * * * * *

The whole problem with the world is that fools and fanatics are always so certain of themselves, and wiser people so full of doubts.

— Bertram Russell

At 9 PM on the nail we were rocking along in pitch darkness in a spluttering wooden motorboat worn with age. We chose the old man of few words who called himself Barbanegra (Blackbeard), and his vessel, out of a dozen who were available for hire in the dockland area below the main bridge. We figured he knew the lay of the land, or rather water, like the back of his hands. Our instructions were to hug the banks of Paraguay and when a beam of high-powered light shone on us, to immediately make our way over to the indicated site. Once there, we were to heed voice commands for further orders.

It's a 50% pure floating-along feeling of adrenalin and a 50% raw stuck-to the-spot fear. You are fighting an unseen enemy outside yourself, but inside you are fighting yourself, too. Sometimes one end wins – but usually it falls somewhere in the middle of the gut, twisting it tighter.

We did this routine twice in the first 20 minutes, following the live instructions shouted at us. Both times we dropped the plastic bag into a reinforced elongated green net of the kind used by anglers. In both cases a burly man holding the handle was wearing a balaclava. I had no doubt he was wearing a bullet-proof metal vest as well. I heard no one else during the transactions. Through my Russian-made night vision flir goggles, (I'd managed to buy them that afternoon from a backstreet 'second-hand' goods dealer, who clearly specialised in expensive items that had fallen off the back of a truck) I discerned several fluorescent green-highlighted armed individuals standing around in the near vicinity. As a former NOC I was trained in the military technique known as 'dancing', which on clandestine ops was to reduce the size of one's silhouette...and these guys were doing exactly that... As we approached, they dispersed into the dense bush alongside the river bank. It would have been foolish to try anything, so we didn't. We just meekly followed their instructions in Spanish. We were delivery boys after all.

It was pretty creepy out there in the stillness as we moved through the motions, admittedly. Something claustrophobic about the scene despite the wide expanse around us. I couldn't imagine doing this kind of work alone and was happy to have the company of three others. You could hear the sound of loud chattering monkeys that carried across the water from all directions. We saw a couple of heavy splashes on the near side banks, and while nobody uttered a word, I could sense the presence of quite big reptilians nearby. I think I would have freaked out if a large snake had appeared above me as we came under low-lying branches of trees a couple of times. And frogs croaked when the exchanges took place. Plenty of insects buzzing around, too. With the background noises from nature's orchestra, military training kicks in eventually. I had to remain focused and not allow wild thinking to take over my brain. Meanwhile the forehead, neck and the middle of my back were dripping with sticky wetness. It was not from the river's occasional spray but from nervous perspiration. I think dread of the unknown contributes to this state of being, where shadows project a size larger than life with each passing minute.

The third strong flash of steady light came from over on the Brazilian side of the water. The old guy (who actually had a grey beard) motoring his dilapidated dinghy didn't want to head over there. He muttered something about the illegality of landing over there. Ricardo told Barbanegra politely but firmly that we were not actually setting foot in Brazil. Getting across there took a while since we were slowed down by the cross-current. I'd say the route followed a zigzag pattern as he had to navigate with the strong tide pulling and pushing his craft.

While the rancher had reason to complain about his lot, for me the immediate problem at hand was this kidnap case now involved the laws of Brazil. It complicated any solution. I knew then that Argentina would feature later in this crazy jaunt. It was already obvious that the number of personnel we had witnessed thus far, showed there was unlimited money backing them. Everybody had to be paid and they conducted themselves professionally and in stealth. Even the lights they used cost a small fortune. We were out of our league. This was a well-trained army of élite security operators, *especialistas*, we were dealing with, no doubt about it.

And sure enough, after listening to the verbal instructions from the fourth collection party, we had to turn around and head south towards the third jurisdiction. Along the way we passed near the embarkation point, and on our right, we saw the bright lights of Cuidad del Este. I wouldn't have known it, but DPF said that all the accents heard so far were from Colombia. That was interesting! I did know that Colombian-Spanish was the most well-spoken of all those who knew the language, and that the Dominicans bastardised it the most.

A trickle of understanding slowly entered my tired mind as the river carried us in the flow. It wounds me to reflect on this…there are things that should not exist on this earth…because when the seventh and last package was being delivered, two hours after we commenced, inside the outstretched net was an unmistakable white item. Same scenario as the other six began to unfold, but this time the voice we heard instructed us to take the envelope out first and then drop the plastic bag inside the webbing. We were bluntly warned that if we didn't faithfully carry out the instructions, we would die. How we would die was never specified. Blackbeard gasped audibly at that moment. But we did as we were told, being in no mood to flaunt our chances for survival whether it be by bullets, drowning or being eaten alive. As the boat was reversing out of a mini-swamp, the same voice said we were completed and were free to head home. At that stage, had there been no message at all, I don't know what words I would have used to pacify the rich rancher upon setting foot again on land.

Once we were back out on open water, DPF read out by torchlight the contents of the note from the bow where he sat. The collection point was designated off the main path in a forest located on some hilly terrain. It was actually not that far from the trucker's stop we had been in before.

In my rush to disembark and run up the gangplank from the boat, I slipped – fortunately landing on my back on the wooden jetty. By the time I limped to the replacement car, where it was parked, the other two were already sitting inside with the engine revving. I dropped into the backseat swearing like a trooper with the pain.

It was a 45-minute ride, mostly in silence, and well after midnight when we arrived at a national park. We parked the car in the unlit empty car park. There wasn't a main footpath but three walkways stared at us through the headlights. Little maps on signs greeted the entrance of each. Fortunately, we were a trio, each one of us had a torch and we set our radios on the same frequency. I went on the path left, DPF took the middle and Ricardo the right. It was eerie, listening to one's own breath and scrunching footsteps on fallen leaves, with the crackling of static into one earpiece. Each sound carried an echo. The flashing light bounced off the oncoming grey. As I went up the slope a light fog enveloped the trail ahead. We took turns calling out for her. What kind of leviathans would leave a frightened young girl up here alone? It was my hope she had been temporarily drugged with a sedative of some sort.

Ricardo's voice reported in that he had reached the top but spotted nothing at all. He'd wait for us to call in once we reached our respective ends. Then a few minutes passed and a breathless DPF did the same. Instinctively I knew in my heart that I would be the one who was going to discover her. *Now I knew why the number three had bugged me from the beginning.*

My spine was really bothering me but I persevered at my limping speed of climb. *It was a tense moment of quiet hush when the flickering light picked out a large black plastic bin bag resting against a tree trunk up ahead.* My watch stated it was 3 o'clock. I shuddered and almost ran the rest of the way despite my hurt. I smelled a bad scent seconds before reaching there but my brain didn't register what it was straightaway. I soon learned the reason… It was the most awful sight I'd ever seen in my life…I'm sure I screamed. She was clearly dead – had been for several days, as rigor mortis had stiffened this bloated puppet-like naked figurine at my feet…and an offensive condom hung grotesquely out of her gaping mouth. A part of her ivory leg sticking out of the bag bore several red bites. She had been fed on by a wild animal since being dumped here.

I sank to my knees and vomited then. I was so numb from the macabre scene of this dead, decaying doll, lying there in front of me…that I couldn't bring myself to alert my colleagues of my PID (positive identification). I retched again. I don't know long it was before I became aware of the other two standing behind me, covering their mouths, eyes wide at what was in front of me.

There isn't anything more I want to describe here, I'm sorry. Forgive me.

* * * * * * * * *

Three days after claiming the body back from the coroner, the bereaved adoptive father spoke at the funeral service from the church pulpit. His voice cracking with emotion, he quoted Pablo Neruda in the present tense, *"I love you as certain dark things are to be loved, in secret, between the shadows and the soul."* There was a long uncomfortable stillness after his eulogy and many of the congregation wept then. My gut shifted discernibly at the time. I have never forgotten those powerful words, spoken with such deep adoration for the beloved step-daughter he lost in the most despicable way possible.

"Grief is the price of losing love," a tearful DPF, who was next to me in the pew, whispered almost to himself.

Outside, in the garden of remembrance, an inconsolable Ricardo came up with a beauty of his own, "Love is where the stream from the mountain flows pure and invigorating…"

That job was to be my last one in K&R in the Americas, for the reason that I am a father too. The experience shattered my spirits and put into question my continued belief in humanity. It was my finale in the dirtiest of dirty businesses. I didn't want to continue dealing with the scum of the earth anymore. Her death all seemed meaningless in the bigger scheme of things. A beautiful young lady is kidnapped then executed in order to prevent her step-father from revealing some incendiary information on criminal activities in high places. Still unnamed influential people were illegally siphoning public funds. The immoral elements not only snuffed the life of an innocent girl, but also destroyed the lives of her parents. *He was a man who knew too much and that was the price he paid.*

The concluding assessment for my employers was it was not a successful result, obviously, more an epic fail. Element of risk involved: minimal. And a heck of a lot of frustration. Followed by the resignation of El Mosquetero, me. A piece of him died there.

I never found out who was behind this ugly deed and whether anybody was arrested. Clearly, the *grupo operative*, or operational group, was well-organised and was supported by big money. I felt like a matchstick man among many other matchstick men in a painting. I didn't stick around to uncover the truth and I haven't been back to find out either. I didn't leave details where I could be contacted. I never saw *mi hermanos,* my brothers, again – DPF and Ricardo – after we bade adios at the cemetery. I *hope* the rancher will one day extract retribution for the transgression committed by heartless thugs. *Time is a healer of wounds.*

I know now that failure has a hundred faces. The whole continent is a horror story. It needs to take on another direction, hopefully for the better. In the near future I *hope* to see all of Latin America reach critical mass. Its people's destiny cannot continue to be hostage to plunder and thunder. It's like a disease that is specific to a particular region, because the whole place is sinking under the triple weight of still being the world's centre of incessant kidnapping, ingrained corruption and intense narco-trafficking. Its soul is for sale, always.

Hope. I know it's only one simple word. But after nothing is left, what remains is always hope…

Vengeance for the blood of a little child.
Satan has not yet created.

– Hayim Nahman Bialik, poet

* * * * * * * * *

Chapter Seven

It was around the turn of the century when I found myself with a bit of free time on my hands and a desire to travel and revisit old haunts in Switzerland. I had, after all, served there in a Secret Intelligence Service spy station for five years during the 1970s.

On the last day of my trip, I decided to take a tour of Geneva. On that sunny day, I was strolling at a leisurely pace around the magnificent Place des Nations, alongside the many other tourists walking around the open space. A square of shooting fountains takes up a corner of the vast plaza. Next to the water fountains, stands a monumental and unconventional sculpture known as *The Broken Chair*. Rising to a height of over 10 meters, this giant wooden chair with its partially splintered leg dominates the flat surrounding area. The pairing of the water jets and the broken chair must symbolise something noble but I didn't know what at the time. I later learned that the work of art was dedicated to Handicap International and intended to rally support for a treaty to ban landmines.

I stood there in awe and for a long while marvelled at the towering structure rising up above the ground. From the corner of my eyes, I caught a glimpse of a large tent that had been set up a short distance away. As I approached the tent, several Middle Eastern women cheerfully greeted me. Though evidently westernised – no one wearing headdress of any kind – I could not but notice that these women were still wearing their colourful traditional flowing robes *(abayas)*. The sight of the old tribal dress-codes against the backdrop of modern civilisation intrigued me. In fact, curiosity is a weakness of mine. After exchanging a few pleasantries, I asked one of the ladies about the reason and the purpose for their presence. Seemingly, they were at the site to demonstrate on behalf of oppressed Muslim women in the Middle East and to raise awareness of the silent suffering of these women.

Sadly, much of what they told me about the ruthless ways of some Muslim nations, I already knew. The notion that the *Qur'an* (Koran) itself or its fanatic adherents would somehow defend them, had long been thoroughly discredited. Their plight reminded me of the 300-year search for the Northwest Passage to find a navigable way from the Atlantic to the Pacific. In sympathy for their cause I gave them my contact details…

About a week later, I received a phone call and this is how this voyage of discovery got underway.

* * * * * * * * *

In the blink of an eye, fast forward to 2014. I had been retired for seven years from the SIS, though I later volunteered for a short but critical field job in 2008. The following year (in late-2009) I finally got to work with the man who had initially solicited me and eventually recruited me to carry out the first of two missions of mercy.

After a long gap, I was now sitting again in his classy office and getting ready to undertake an ambitious sequel to the original quest. I listened intently to the Iranian-born, nattily-dressed man. He was the head of a Geneva-based non-governmental organization (NGO). He explained in great detail the differences between the two Iranian flags that existed. I'd been to Iran twice before and thought I knew a lot about the place. I hadn't noticed the differences before but it wasn't like I had a habit of focusing that closely on the ensigns of other countries.

Each one told its own story. The green, white and red horizontal bands stood respectively for Islam, peace and bravery. At first glance, both flags seem to be identical. But a closer look reveals the key differences in their design. The Islamic Republic version has in its centre the word 'Allah' written in red and in a pattern that evokes the shape of a tulip. In contrast, the other flag has an imaginative gold-coloured lion depicted on it with a golden sun serving as a backdrop. This particular emblem was adopted by the Iranian resistance and currently represents the socialist-minded exiles belonging to the Shia branch of Islam. They are now scattered around the world and live in 22 countries.

I was inside their high-security building overlooking Lac Léman. The building, as well as the budget for the NGO, was largely funded by their wealthiest member. I had consulted for the council once before. Back in 2009 I had signed a lifetime non-disclosure agreement, so I am not at liberty to disclose the identity of the NGO nor the name of its chief benefactor. I will only say that some of you may have heard of him. He is a modest and humble man who currently lives in the eastern region of Germany. He is also devoted to his followers and their cause. But he absolutely refuses to accept any credit for the humanitarian mission he was about to sponsor privately for the second time in five years.

There are certain operational details I still cannot divulge without violating the terms of my confidentiality agreement. *Yet I feel deeply that this story needs to be chronicled, so the public is made aware that such acts of magnanimity and generosity do indeed take place from time to time.* I can also disclose that the council and its chief patron have fully endorsed and supported the *Mujahedeen-e-Khalq* (abbreviated as MEK) also known as the People's Mujahedeen Organisation of Iran (PMOI). They are a left-wing group, who in their time actively opposed not just the Shah of Iran but also the Ayatollahs, whom they regarded as ultraconservative or very right wing. "Spiritually un-Persian like," were the exact words the head of the NGO had uttered in my presence. In its broadest definition *mujahedeen* means 'warriors of the Muslim faith' but in the west the term has taken the meaning of guerrillas or insurgents. Others would describe them as Marxist freedom fighters or revolutionaries. They are not extremists or terrorists by any means. Quite the contrary. They actually believe in equal rights for women and in many respects, can be considered as the most liberal and open-minded sect among Islam's various factions. In the early days, their original red on white logo portrayed a sickle crossing a rifle with a red star hovering above them. Nowadays, the modern gold lion and sun have replaced the original logo. To the outsider, the proliferation of flags and symbols can get a bit confusing but they do reflect the undying beliefs held by their respective supporters.

From the outset, I had to keep the proposed endeavour in absolute secrecy. If I accepted the job being offered to me again, I would once more have access to nearly unlimited financing to successfully pull it off. They naturally requested me to submit a game plan at 'my earliest convenience'. I understood that request to mean 'please work with haste as time is of the essence'. The NGO head then added ominously that the Iraqi army was now starting to kill his co-religionists for blood-sport. I don't know if the non-profit fellow had any sense of humour or not, but in this same meeting, he mentioned that Iran's main national holiday falls on 1 April. I had to laugh at that!

* * * * * * * * *

I had flown that morning from my home on the French Riviera. The EasyJet flight had taken off from Nice and within a short hour I landed in Geneva. (I flew back that same day into Nice.) My Iranian hosts naturally paid for all my expenses just as they did the last time around. On the return journey, I filled my carry-on bag with all sorts of juicy information to help me carry out the plan that the Iranian expatriates were asking me to execute. In short order and for the second time in five years, I was tasked with securing the release and evacuation of several hundred Iranian citizens from a camp called Liberty, near Baghdad's international airport in Iraq. Many of those refugees had been stranded for decades. The younger ones had been born in captivity and had never known any place other than a refugee camp.

They had previously lived in another encampment named Ashraf for 26 years. The camp lay 40 kilometres north of the Iraqi capital and 80 kilometres west of the Iranian border. It's a rather long story how they ended up at that location. In a nut shell, they were left-leaning Shias escaping political persecution from extreme right Sunni factions. As matters stand, the Shia minority and the Sunni majority have plenty of religious issues to fight over. The conflict could be exacerbated if political sensitivities or nationalistic elements are added to the mix. As was often the case throughout history, such toxic conditions can become a fertile ground for pent-up tension that could trigger, at any time, violent confrontations between religious factions or even open warfare between sovereign nations.

Five years earlier, we were only partially successful in achieving our objectives. At the time, we negotiated the release of a small batch of refugees that included eight young women and 18 children between the ages of 9 and 14 who had no parents to care for them. The helicopter we flew on landed in Camp Ashraf (named after the Princess, the Shah of Iran's rebellious sister). We had already nine people on board for the return trip. The three cockpit seats were occupied by the pilot, myself and the interpreter. The other seats were taken by six Brits. With all of us on board, the space for actual passengers was limited. We figured that by squeezing two kids to a seat, the whirlybird could accommodate just 26 refugees on its return journey. The lucky passengers were quickly selected by the local council of elders. But before we could take off, we still had to secure travel documents for the evacuees. None of them had any paperwork other than an Iraqi identification card with their name and photo on it. An international charity for women refugees helped us secure emergency travel documents. For its efforts, the aid agency received a substantial donation from the NGO in Geneva, who had in turn received the funds from the wealthy donor. All this was organised rather quickly after I placed a call on the satellite phone from the middle of nowhere and in the dead of night. Those 26 evacuees, ironically, represented the 26 years that many of those left behind had been stuck in Iraq.

There was a happy ending to this undertaking. Those rescued went on to live in the Netherlands. Upon arrival, the refugees sought asylum and the Netherlands generously opened their doors for them. Documents were filed on their behalf to show they would be financially well-supported and would not be a burden on the Dutch state. I understand that the same refugees have grown up to be young adults. They are now living free in every sense of the word and productively contributing to society. Needless to say, I am proud to have been a part of the cogs that made their liberation possible. To my pleasant surprise, the head of the NGO in Geneva presented me with a recent group photograph of the emancipated group taken in Amsterdam's Dam Square. It must have been a blustery day as they all looked like a bunch of western women and teenagers with their hair blown all over the place. They were all dressed in fashionable clothes and were grinning from ear to ear – free as the wind! Seeing the group having a good time, made me feel good.

* * * * * * * * * *

I'd been to Iraq a few times before and I knew all too well that the Iraqis and the Iranians did not have any love for each other. Their nationalistic-driven animosities went back decades to say the least. The deep-seated hatred between them had only exacerbated over the years. The background reading material given to me on the long-standing conflict and my own research on the internet, confirmed that the entire state of affairs was probably the most complex and volatile I'd ever seen in my life. Every prior diplomatic or political attempt to diffuse and solve this particular refugee crisis, had ended in failure. The gulf between the parties was such that their worlds ran on a widely different set of rules. Call it bureaucratic plodding, if you like. But innocents were needlessly dying with each passing day. It was time to take action *without rules*. I felt a deep sense of moral imperative. Yet I had to consider the significant risk to me and any member of my yet to be selected team. After all, the whole region was now engulfed in civil unrest and violent demonstrations that came to be known as the Arab Spring uprising.

I switched into my usual inner-debate mode with myself: *My spirit had mellowed considerably with age.* But the older I'd got, the better I was at analysing and strategizing complex issues. *Throughout my SIS career my job had been to make order out of chaos.* I'd been described as both intense and relaxed, which is a contradiction in terms. I always used to think that everything was relative. The so-called informed opinion held by others, sitting comfortably at their desk, often did not take into account what was actually going on in the field of play where I was. *So generally, because I knew, hand over heart, from experience that many things can go wrong out there, this kind of unusual circumstance could become a case of managed pessimism on the spot. Yet I knew full well that without optimism, we wouldn't get there anyway!*

A welcome change for the better had taken place since the last time we were in Iraq. In the intervening time, several hundred members of the MEK/PMOI had been relocated to Camp Liberty (*Hurriya* in Arabic), near Baghdad international airport. That location was a hell of a lot more accessible than Camp Ashraf. I was immediately thinking that with proper organisation, we could fly them all out in aircrafts that would land in the fully functioning airport. But where would they go? Who would take hundreds of stateless refugees and grant them asylum? I realised that I was getting ahead of myself. I had other things to worry about before having to cross that proverbial bridge.

The very next day, I accepted the offer to consult for the NGO a second time. I submitted a general action plan within hours. With bullet points, I ironically stressed that if we were shot at or the lives of my team were endangered, we would stop dead in our tracks and turn back. The last time, the bunch of hires I took got into a raging firefight with an unknown Iraqi group wearing no uniforms. It was a close shave. But 26 young people are free today, in the west, as a result of that success.

* * * * * * * * *

The Swiss-based NGO representing the Iranian expatriates agreed to all the terms I had specified. No real difference from the last time. Initial funds were wired to me at once. I expected to receive confirmation that the money was indeed deposited into my bank account within 1-3 days. Financial institutions as well as stock brokerage firms refer to this lag as a 'settlement period'. While awaiting my bank to confirm the deposit, I proceeded to contact by e-mail six British former special forces buddies I had served with from 2003 through 2007 in Iraq, Iran, Somalia, Yemen and Afghanistan. This particular bunch of warriors had now retired from active duty, like I had. I knew what they were capable of. A few other individuals had left the service as well. I went with the lads that, in my opinion, had pulled through those crazy times without a hint of post-traumatic stress disorder (PTSD). In the old days, the armed forces had labelled symptoms of PTSD as LMF (lack of moral fibre). At least progress had been made to treat those who had suffered in the service of queen and country. *The fractured world was changing slowly for the better, but negative elements were still fighting a rear-guard battle and resisting any progress. You just can't throw young men into the cesspool of war and expect them to come out mentally unscathed from their horrific ordeals on the battlefield.*

Now we were going to serve a 'country' that didn't exist yet, and may never. I explained the unconventional nature of the upcoming operation to each one of the selected fighters. First and foremost, I needed them to agree to drop whatever they were currently doing in their daytime civilian jobs and commit to 10 days away from their families. I took pains to explain their involvement wasn't mercenary work but an emergency humanitarian mission. They would be amply rewarded in cash for their time, with all-expenses assumed. Each team member would be covered by life insurance in the event the unthinkable happens. Amazingly, all six of them were only too eager to participate. Three of them owned their own small businesses. Two others took advantage of holiday time they were entitled to. The sixth candidate was currently unemployed. I got a sense that all of them missed the adrenaline rushes.

I had an unusual request for the lad from Nottingham. I asked him if he could purchase four cricket bags in any condition (new, second-hand or rejects) from a local manufacturer ironically named Gunn & Moore (heard in the local accent as 'guns 'n' more'). I remembered him once telling me way back when that he had a family member who worked at the company. I naturally promised to reimburse him for any outlay he would incur. He responded that the factory was indeed close by. He would pop over straightaway and see what he could do. But true to his British Army and Special Air Service training, it had not even occurred to him to enquire about the reason for the request from his former commanding officer.

There is only so much planning one can do upfront. For a job of this kind there is a lot of playing it by ear. I needed the kind of people that had the personalities to go with the flow and the ability to improvise when necessary.

By the next day, all six had flown into Nice Côte d'Azur (NCE). They respectively came from Belfast, Cardiff, Edinburgh, Manchester, Newcastle and Nottingham. Thank goodness there were lots of cheap air connections from the UK to the South of France. A good friend of mine who had moved to the Nice area from Wales, lived near the airport. He was enlisted to provide transportation services to the lads. In return for petrol money and reimbursement of airport parking fees, he kindly collected each one of them individually in his SUV. He then drove them one at a time to a small hotel on the nearby Promenade des Anglais. I knew the French girl who ran the guesthouse. I had lived there for six months, a few years before. She agreed to quickly reserve the rooms without requiring an upfront deposit, simply based on my say so over the phone. I paid her in euros in full once we met, of course. A breakfast for all was kindly thrown in gratis. It's nice to have good, reliable people around that you know will jump to it just by ringing them up. I don't want to divulge their names here because I've never asked them if I can. I was tickled pink that some of the Britons still addressed me in person as either 'Boss' or 'Captain Fantastic'! And the lad on the flight from Nottingham had the four empty cricket bags folded in his case. I refunded him the money he had spent on them.

In addition to the six Brits, I enlisted the help of Brian. He was a young Frenchman, who hailed from Marseille. His mother is French and his father a Lebanese Christian. He was to be the translator as he spoke fluent Arabic, French and English. I met him several years ago on the railway platform in Cannes. His mother asked my friend if she could use his mobile/cell to call her son as their train was expected soon. Apparently, Brian was off buying himself clothes in the glitzy shops on the Croisette. Fortunately, he arrived in time to catch the TGV (France's intercity high-speed rail service) home. I seemed to have gelled with Brian from the beginning. He was thrilled that I asked him to join me on this trip to the land of his father. He'd been to Lebanon many times. His father's family still lived in Beirut.

Next was a trip by all of us to the local hypermarket on the other side of the airport. We hopped into the Welshman's car and mine. We bought a bunch of black T-shirts and one pair of black lightweight cotton jeans for each of the eight of us going on the trip. That was when I first learned about BOGOF (buy one, get one free)! Then because the blokes from Britain were all a bit rusty, we headed up into the hills above town to practice some drills without arms, translator from France and me included. I was surprised how fit each of the Brits were, considering that they had been out of the military for a couple of years. In my case, it had been six years since I fully retired from SIS. But I had kept fit by following a strict regime of physical activities that included a healthy dose of swimming, football, bicycling and badminton. A little-known fact about badminton is that the special forces of many countries actually provide a racquet and a tube of shuttlecocks to all members to encourage them to play the game regularly. It is said to improve eye to hand coordination. The Red Army was a strong proponent of badminton, while the British military generally shied away from the game. Not surprisingly, the young Frenchman was the least fit among the team. Our genial middle-aged Welsh driver didn't participate at all in the drill. He only laughed heartily at our exertion.

That evening we discussed the usual game plans – A through to F. I reminded everybody that mobile/cell phones were easily trackable and could disclose our location within an accuracy of 4 metres (13 feet). I asked them to be ready to disconnect the battery upon my instructions to do so. There was no longer a need for the football code names we each had before. Nom de guerre's beginning with the same letter of the alphabet as the person's real name was also debated and rejected. I was happy they had not forgotten their in-bred culture of learning. The off-beat was still there, too. I thought the best line of the day was when one of the lads wryly remarked about his teenage sons, "For kids today playing computer games, it must be disappointing when they come back to reality."

As for Brian, his comment at the end of the day was also memorable: "This is life entering a whole new world I never knew existed!"

The next day we all caught a seasonal direct Middle East Airlines flight from NCE to Beirut. Within 48 hours of contacting my former colleagues and finding an interpreter, we were all already on the ground in the theatre of operations. I dealt with the same people as I did the last time I was in Beirut. While there, we 'rented' the weapons we would need for our protection during the task. Ironically, the supplier of the arms turned out to be none other than the Hezbollah (Party of God), a faction allied to and backed by the government of Iran. *But they didn't need to know about our activities, and they didn't ask.* The deal, as before, was a simple verbal rental agreement with a refundable security deposit. The lads quickly checked out the equipment we received, dismantling and re-assembling it in front of the Lebanese. From the impressed faces of the locals I could see that they thought the Britons were seasoned handlers of fire power. They'd just witnessed a full-scale demonstration of mastery and precision.

Shortly afterwards, and packed into two taxis, we headed to the heliport. A Scottish voice in the back of my cab exclaimed, "Ever noticed that the more east you go, people talk louder!" The quip made everybody laugh.

I'm glad I anticipated the requirement for personal air transport as being the single biggest expense. It had been the case the last time around. The people in Switzerland had already taken care of the US$5 million security deposit and the insurance premium in Lebanon. The security deposit would naturally be refunded upon the return of one helicopter in functioning condition. Shortly after our arrival in Beirut we boarded the chartered helicopter for our next leg of the trip. The overhauled Mi-8MTV-1 Russian-made chopper had been, until its retirement, part of the Russian military's air fleet. It was now piloted by a miserable Czech chap, who only communicated in monosyllabic words. Fortunately, he uttered some of them in English and Arabic. The heli rental company, we were told, flew regularly to and from Beirut and Damascus and had prior clearance to enter Syrian airspace provided its aircraft stayed in the approved air lanes.

Getting from Damascus to Baghdad was somewhat trickier because the border separating Syria and Iraq was now a conflict zone, with hostilities raging on the ground and above. Air lanes were still open to commercial traffic. The problem was that our bird, with its past history, still looked very much like a military machine. We could easily be mistaken as belonging to an enemy air force. It was a risk we had to take.

As the crow flies, the distance between the two Arab capitals was 750 km. but the fastest route was actually 69 km longer. We had to take the longer route to avoid becoming the target of anti-aircraft batteries deployed in the area. The Mi-8 was fitted with XL drop tanks to hold extra fuel. Still, it had a maximum range of just under 1,110 km. We would need to refuel at Baghdad airport to make the return trip or find another way around this nagging problem. *This was the Achilles heel of the entire operation.* It wasn't good to broadcast the fact that I didn't know the answer just yet.

Our unnamed Czech pilot did not immediately address the issue either, or he didn't tell me about his solution. But I knew something about choppers myself. I had, after all, flown them once. To my mind, his craft was far from being in perfect condition. Its fuselage was pockmarked with impacts from rounds of ammunition. You'd think they'd plug the holes at least, to make the chopper more presentable. But I was more preoccupied with the quandary of not having enough fuel to make the return trip safely. *Sometimes it's best to say nothing but still consider the problem as your own. You prepare yourself to deal with it quietly if the main man doesn't, minimising surprises at all times. You don't address difficulty by ignoring it.*

How the chap got around the issue of not having enough fuel flabbergasted me. He illegally loaded several containers of highly-inflammable fuel inside the cabin where we were strapped in for the flight! If we ever got hit by a missile, we wouldn't feel a damn thing! Turned to cinder in a second. Even more worrisome was the sight of the pilot holding the 'stick' (cyclic-pitch lever) with a death grip that made his knuckles white. For heaven's sake, he didn't have to hold it so hard. I still didn't say anything to anybody else. Was he nervous? He was certainly making me nervous! Sitting next to him in the cockpit, without a helmet, only added to my discomfort. But we made it safely to Damascus where we were reserved for the night in a reasonably nice hotel outside the heliport.

Right after dinner in the small hotel restaurant, a hotel clerk approached me while I was drinking a cup of mud-like Turkish coffee. I always sit facing the entrance. Nearly everybody had turned in for the night, but two remained with me as I had requested. Brian and the Englishman from Nottingham came with me to the lobby. As I was expecting, three well-dressed Syrian visitors greeted us. We all shook hands but we did not exchange names. I duly signed twice on the dotted lines of two official-looking one-page documents in Arabic they presented me with. One was my copy to keep. After another round of handshakes, the trio swiftly left, leaving the eight sealed cardboard boxes where they were on the floor. We carried the hefty boxes up in the lift to my room. I gave a nice tip to the hotel clerk who had helped us carry the boxes.

The British lad went off down the corridor and returned with the four new cricket bags he had bought in his home town. It took us a while to sort out all the cash we had in front of us and neatly repack it. When we were finished, we had a cool US$4 million of cash in our hands divided equally in four different bags, including filling all the side pockets. It was sight to behold. In each bag, we stacked a hundred packets of US$10,000 in used $100 bills. Each bag weighed a bit over 22 pounds. I know this because I put one of them on the scales at the heliport in the morning then informed the pilot of the 88 pounds of extra load.

In this region of the world, the payment of *backsheesh* (Arabic for bribe or tip) is a normal practice on the streets. The offer of cash can miraculously open doors and expedite services. It can also buy the silence of the mouth. Does not work all the time, though.

I should add that the remit for my British compatriots on the ground was first and foremost, to protect the four ordinary looking cricket bags full of used US dollar bills. Beyond that, the lads needed to cover my back the rest of the time! We'd be needing the magic lure of the greenbacks when we got to Baghdad. We certainly didn't need the unwanted attention of anybody while we were passing through the Syrian capital either!

It was an uncomfortable night with the entire area around the Syrian capital on a war footing. We were warned that the electricity would be switched off by 10 PM. Occasionally, the lights flickered and bright flashes lit the sky above. The soundtrack of the Arab Spring uprising could be heard in the distance. From time to time, the lull was shattered by loud booms of unknown provenance.

* * * * * * * * *

We were all up and about early the next morning. After a good full Middle Eastern breakfast, we were all set for the second leg.

The highest altitude the Mi-8 could fly was 14,765 feet and we were flying pretty close to that ceiling. The silent moments of the flight weren't really silent. Sitting inside a metal tube I had to contend with the insanely loud noise of the rotor drowning any attempt for a meaningful conversation. I wondered what sins the Iranian refugees committed to deserve the fate that befell them. Was it true that Iraqi soldiers were taking pot shots at them as a macabre form of entertainment? *Hatred is a funny thing.* We soon crossed over the border between Syria and Iraq. From up there and looking through binoculars, their national flags had a striking resemblance to each other. The Iraqi flag has one squiggle in the middle of the white horizontal strip while the Syrian has two spots… Despite the similarity, both stirred up enough passion among their believers to be willing to die for. Just as the Iranian flag(s) did.

Anbar province, from the Syrian border eastwards to Baghdad, is almost all flat terrain. A desert, dotted with remote oil installations all surrounded by high walls and razor wire. From up there, the ground below reminded me of a brown carpet covered with stains. Slowly the rural areas outside the Iraqi capital crept into view as our Czech pilot began his descent into BGW (Baghdad International Airport), some 16 km west of the city centre. When I first saw it in 2003, it used to be called Saddam International Airport, with the appropriate code SAD. During my last visit in 2009, the

US Army was in the midst of a gradual withdrawal of troops from Iraq. Two years later they were all but gone. But Islamic State was raising its ugly head and by 2014 the Americans had returned to help fight the scourge.

For most people the adrenaline starts to kick-in when the targeted site comes into view. But mine goes the other way. Frames begin to move slower. I become calmer before the storm and I deliberately go deeper within myself. Perhaps all this takes place because I am responsible for the lives around me. I call it my zombie zone. I am deadly focused, yet I remain almost serene under pressure. In short, I adopt the attitude of so be it, or come what may.

As we were coming down into the heli zone, I could just about see where Camp Liberty's wall touched the airport perimeter. The modern airport terminal looked the same. New Iraqi Airways jets in green and white livery were parked on the tarmac. The national airline had ceased operations in 2010, partly due to claims for compensation from Kuwait arising out of the First Gulf War. Further away were the gunmetal colours of US Air Force transports. After the helicopter's engine died, we each put on our ballistic body armour. As we filed out of the Mi-8, the midday heat hit us with a vengeance. Iraqi immigration agents simply waved us through. They had no interest in us at all. I hoped they would exhibit the same lack of interest when we were on our way out, inside 24-48 hours' time. We had dismantled any weaponry we had and placed the parts in the various rucksacks and the luggage we carried. I kept my loaded pistol tucked in the back of my trousers' belt with my jacket covering the piece. I was sure the Iraqi uniforms knew full well we were mostly military guys. Well, ex-servicemen in our case. They'd seen enough of our type come through over the years. In some ways it was in our favour that Muslim extremism was on the rise. We weren't the enemy within. Their focus was elsewhere.

An amiable, well-turned out, fresh-faced, young man holding the name of the Swiss non-profit on a piece of cardboard, met us in the arrival hall. Remember, please, I am under a confidentiality agreement. I do know his name but will not write it here. Brian and the lad were about the same age. They both had this endearing kind of innocence about them. They could presumably walk unknowingly through a minefield, come out the other side unscathed, and not know the dangers they'd just evaded... Hey-ho, I wished I could be like that!

We were led to a mini-bus waiting for us. The grim-faced, elderly driver then took us for the short ride over to Camp Liberty. It was a different feel in Baghdad after the clinging fear that gripped us during the invasion in 2003. The years that followed didn't improve, as hatred of anything foreign ruled the mind-sets of the locals. I'd come again briefly in 2009 and, while the atmosphere had slightly improved, there was still a residual and discernible animosity towards those who weren't from here.

Suddenly, I felt the annals of negative history briefly lifting off my shoulders. An Iraqi kid standing there roadside and selling fruit near the airport gate, animatedly waved at us in genuine happiness. Some of the British lads returned his greetings. We all smiled at each other. With this lovely physical poetry, we felt like we had just made our own little contribution towards world peace. I couldn't remember having seen a local kid look so upbeat. At that moment I wanted to imagine future Iraqi generations living in freedom from dictatorship and occupying forces (I was one of them). Sadly, Islamic State (known locally as Daesh) and other extremists were working hard at reintroducing the numbness and pain from the past. The stuttering march towards lasting peace would have to be temporarily put on hold to stop the crawl back to the age of medievalism. I sighed. It seemed that the same dark sentiment could be applied to these Iranians stuck in Iraq.

The traffic was bad as I remembered it. Exhaust fumes and choking dust everywhere. Women wearing full-length black chadors (face is seen) and burkas (mesh over eyes) in the midday sun because the controlling men wanted them to protect their modesty. As the bus entered the camp, guarded by a lone Iraqi policeman, a group of local hecklers were screaming at the gate. Some of them banged on our windows. I asked Brian what they were saying. He blushed, *"Inshallah yishrbu waridat al-nisa?* It's a curse, I think it means, may they drink menstrual blood."

Once inside, a group of elderly chaps who were obviously waiting for our arrival, rushed out of the shade to kiss each and every one of us three times on the cheeks. I was truly gratified by the warm welcome after that jolt on the senses. All my prior tours in the country had been nothing but strenuous and stressful from beginning to end. This time, however, despite the welcome outside, the feeling was far more pleasurable! Despite the fuzzy good feeling, there was still an underlying sense of danger. All the Brits present were battle-hardened and knew all too well how things could turn in an instant. Fresh on our mind was an incident that occurred there a week earlier. Some Iraqis had evidently driven into the camp and ran over half a dozen innocent souls. Or as Brian translated, with his index finger pointing to the ceiling, "They are now the virgins in paradise, *janna*." The law of Iraq couldn't be bothered with their deaths. The victims were, after all, Iranians. The Iraqis wanted them out, but couldn't get rid of them.

Some shy, pretty, smiling teenaged girls with long dark hair served us tea and biscuits. They were not wearing headdresses of any kind. *At that moment, I had a flashback of those that made it out to Holland. The happiness on their faces was etched into my memory. In my mind, it was a glimpse of what freedom could look like for these wretched people. They had suffered so much, and yet could still manage a smile. I was thinking then that I only want to contribute to the future of others from hereon in. No going backwards.*

Brian and the young interpreter, whom we met at the airport, were busy boys communicating what was being said. The *emir*, their leader, had already compiled the list of those who would go free with us. "God willing", he intoned with hands in the air. Some of these girls in the room were on the list. But my mind wandered somewhere else. "Why can't everybody leave?" I asked. The chief looked at me like the thought had never crossed his mind. "It is impossible," he stated. Then he sheepishly asked, "How? There would still be about 200 left, if and when this next group had departed."

Right then, I glanced out of the window and watched an Iraqi Airways wide-body touching down. The old man followed my eyes and saw it, too. As if he was reading my mind, he said that the airline only flew within the Middle East. He didn't want anybody going to any Arab country, naturally. But I was thinking outside the box. Any one of several Muslim lands outside the region could take them and probably receive generous financial support for its efforts. I was thinking of Albania, Bosnia & Herzegovina, Bulgaria, Kosovo or European mainland Turkey. Even Cuidad del Este, an enclave of liberal-minded Muslims in Paraguay could be considered as a destination for the refugees! Venezuela, too! The elder kept looking at me as if I was unhinged and said something about Allah. Brian apparently couldn't translate what he said. His new buddy just looked down at the floor. As an atheist I interpreted the situation as I had long believed, that religion hinders human potential.

In any case, I had already decided that I wasn't going to do the same as before. The status quo wasn't working and was no longer acceptable. We had a remit to end a world of hurt. To me, the chief and his cronies had obviously developed the so-called Stockholm Syndrome. They had formed a psychological attachment to their captors as a survival strategy during their prolonged imprisonment. The symptoms can be observed during a hostage situation, when the victims begin to identify with the takers.

We had to rise to the challenge and take the bull by its horns! Clearly the Iranian elders needed a few mad dogs to stir up the pot and get this ball rolling in the right direction, out of Iraq. *You cannot play this game by others' rule book.* This Englishman dared to defy convention and take a road not yet travelled.

Soon after this exchange with the chief, I assembled a small group and we headed back to the airport in the mini-bus for a recce. I took three of my lads and the two terps with me. I overheard one of the Brits say to the pair of bewildered younger fellows, "Well he's like a cat. You don't know what he's going to do next!" The driver stayed with the vehicle. I wanted to snoop around to learn where flights were going to and coming from. *You make your own luck.* Within the hour, we discovered that two charter airlines were bringing in much needed goods twice a week but were returning empty. One aircraft originated in Serbia while the other was from Pakistan.

It wasn't long before I knocked on the door of the unmarked office belonging to a Serbian company. It was located on the top floor of the airport terminal. The whole place lacked air-conditioning of any kind. A sweaty, overweight fellow who wasn't Iraqi grunted at me when he answered the door. He was pre-prepared to dismiss me at once, regardless of who I was or whether I had a valid reason for disrupting his schedule. The others stayed outside as instructed. I brazenly walked in and, without asking, took a seat. I asked the bloke if he spoke English. He did. *You have to strike while the iron is hot.* I came straight to the point. I would pay his company handsomely to fly goods out of Iraq to Serbia. Got his attention immediately. The greed factor kicked in.

If you don't open your mouth and ask, you don't get anything. From the one-hour meeting that followed, I gathered many details. The plane was a modified Airbus cargo jet. It was operated by a crew of four (the pilot, co-pilot, the third officer and the quartermaster). It had no windows nor seats, just storage racks and straps to prevent crates from shifting during flight. I stipulated that the aircraft had to be parked at a certain strategic spot so we could load the merchandise more efficiently. He didn't flinch at any of my requests. Everything was possible. This was Iraq in wartime all over again, he simply shrugged! He was a part-owner and could decide anything. The aircraft was actually due to land first thing tomorrow morning. We agreed on maintaining absolute secrecy. We discussed the weight of the stock that would be loaded. I invented some imaginary number because I simply didn't know. I assured the Serbian that my people at the other end would pay all taxes and import duty to Serbian customs. I even signed a piece a paper to that effect. When I left, he was grinning widely at his good fortune because I was going to pay him in cash one hour before departure! At no time did I describe the nature of the cargo. I certainly refrained from mentioning that the aircraft would be transporting people. That would have suggested I was a human trafficker. The paperwork I would present to him the next day would have to include legitimate documents. I didn't have that part yet.

It was the best bit of business I'd done in quite a while, if I say so myself!

＊ ＊ ＊ ＊ ＊ ＊ ＊ ＊ ＊

Now on a wing and a prayer, you have to make it work!

Like the last time, I got on the blower (satellite phone) to update the head of the Swiss non-profit. He promised to immediately activate a six-person rapid deployment team (6RDT) to the specialty cargo area at Belgrade airport. I could not exactly specify how many people would make the trip with us, but I would attempt to evacuate the maximum possible. I ventured to guess that at least half of the camp population would still remain in Iraq after we had left. Hopefully, another operation could be organised at a later date to pick up the remaining refugees and take them to a place of safety.

We would, of course, take as many as we could back with us on the helicopter. A separate 2RDT (two rapid responders) were assigned as well. They would be on standby in Beirut for our arrival. Once again, I thanked my good fortune for the potential break. A lot was riding on our ability to locate a working fax machine somewhere in Baghdad. We would need to properly receive the authorisation documents to persuade the Serbians that their arse was legally covered.

I stayed in the camp and sent the two intrepid interpreters out in the mini-bus, along with the hapless driver and a pair of armed Brit bodyguards – for close protection. They were on a search and locate assignment of huge importance. The five of them were tasked to find a bloody facsimile machine with plenty of paper in it. Finding a fax in a place that was at war with others, and itself, was no easy feat, as the locals would argue over the most trivial of things to hold back progress. I gave them plenty of cash and the satellite phone. They would call Switzerland once they had located a working unit, and wait there for the transmission to come in. Their young, eager faces told me they were up for it. For Brian, it was the biggest adventure in his short lifetime. He wasn't going to flunk it.

Meanwhile, we had to organise who was going on the plane and the chopper and who wasn't. The selection process was quite stressful for the refugees and us. It was perhaps the most painful of tasks to witness the range of emotions among the refugees. Those selected were naturally elated. I could sense that some in-camp politics were at play, despite the fact that the language spoken was foreign to me. Only one bag per person to be permitted. Unusually, the estimated weight of the individual was asked and became a factor for consideration.

The fax crew eventually returned after dusk. They had been away for four fucking hours. I was beginning to be concerned about their welfare. I sweated! Job done. I didn't want to learn how, just that they did the job required of them, yay. They all looked exhausted…in the quest to receive a simple fax. They placed in my hands plenty of paperwork to read that evening. The Swiss end had come through admirably once again and they did so on short notice.

* * * * * * * * *

As dawn broke, out of the endless blue I saw the silent spot in the sky slowly looming towards us. Its lights were off for security reasons. An all-white cargo jet glided down on BGW's main runway right in front of where I was standing. Its country code clearly seen –YU followed by three alphabet letters. YI was Iraq, I had already learned. I wasn't alone looking at this spectacle. I turned sideways and at least 50 camp dwellers of all ages were doing the same. Some were praying, others weeping openly, hands were being held, some punched the air.

Long stressful hours passed. By mid-afternoon the Airbus was slowly pulled for two miles to a location just outside the camp's perimeter. This was one of the conditions I had specified for the deal to go through. She was in pretty good nick, clean, like a giant white mother swan floating along on the shimmering surface of the tarmac. The tow vehicle uncoupled itself and drove back to the terminal area. The plane's cargo door swung open and a retracting mechanical gangway started to unfold.

Out came the wire cutter. We cut a hole into the fence that was big enough to allow a person to sneak out. I stepped through and walked at a deliberate pace towards the Serbian. As he disembarked down the staircase, he waved at me. Some other guys followed him down the ramp. Two of my lads followed me out, staying about 10 paces behind. We all stood in a shady spot under the aircraft wing. I was going to rely heavily on my interpretation of the human condition at close quarters. I didn't discern any doubts or negativity. But I detected a certain hunger in his eyes for quick money. With that in mind, I was going to appeal to the 'greed factor'. The Serbian then introduced us to the aircraft crew. We all shook hands cordially. They offered us bottles of distilled cold water and we graciously accepted the refreshing relief. It was bloody hot out there! A well-presented lot. It struck me they were professional in what they did. Or followed orders from their boss. I gathered they must have looked at my two British escorts and me as being the kind of people not to be messed around with. I felt we presented ourselves as honourable people.

So far so good, I thought. I asked the Northern Irish lad to open the cricket bag he carried. While he was going through the motions, I explained that the bag contained precisely one million American dollars in unmarked bills. I then added slowly and deliberately in English, "You cannot put a price on freedom." All five of them peered in at the pile, then looked quizzically at each other. The co-owner then asked what was the exact product that required shipment? I pointed to the group of mostly kids standing and staring at us from behind the wire fence a mere 200 yards away. At the same time, I presented him with a one-page document (and a translation into Serbian of it) known as *pleins pouvoirs* (full powers). It was signed by the German head of state and addressed to the head of the state of Serbia. The form stated that there was a formal recognition of the necessity for absolute confidence in the authority and standing of the negotiator (and my name was typed there), and to do as was asked of them.

How this official document was obtained so quickly is beyond my calling, but there it was, clearly, in black and white in front of this group of Serbians – in their own language. They looked gobsmacked. They had all the good reasons in the world to go along with my request. In the first place, our plan seemed to be supported by their own government. Secondly, a bag of ready cash was within their grasp. Thirdly, Germany did a lot of trade with Serbia, probably their best business partner. And lastly, I was appealing to their humanity.

In cases where an envoy is entrusted with an unusually complex set of tasks that would not be covered by an authoritative permanent delegation, a substitute representative may be designated. As such, he or she is given either limited or full power, according to the requirement of the case at hand. Its usage is a formal recognition of the necessity of absolute confidence in the authority and standing of the negotiator.

Fortunately, they agreed right then to the deal. From that point on, the rest of this drama unfolded in quick order. The flight was logged with the airport tower at short notice. Within two hours, 75 refugees, composed of mostly women and children (including two disabled), holding hands with each other in a chain boarded the aircraft. We were good to go. They flew out on that bird lying on the floor. They somehow evaded the various Iraqi uniforms stationed within plain sight of us. Just over three and a half hours later the group were greeted by the 6RDT from Switzerland. The Serbs even gave them an empty hangar to use. I was informed later that there were two mini-windows on the Airbus to look out of and all the passengers on that plane had never seen the sea before. I stifled a cry when I heard that.

Our trip home on the helicopter took much longer. We picked up 26 refugees and made our way to Beirut after a short stop in Damascus. Along the way we were shot at, but made it back unscathed. In Damascus the same three couriers accepted back three full cricket bags of unused cash. The duo from Switzerland were waiting at the heliport in Beirut. The eight of us then boarded a Cyprus- bound plane, connecting onto our respective destinations. Ironically, after travelling nonstop, an exhausted Brian and I landed in Nice exactly 26 hours after we departed Baghdad. Soon afterwards, the so-called Arab Spring erupted, and violence reached new and never seen before heights.

Not long afterwards I received a nice card from Brian's mum saying her son had left a naïve boy and returned as a man of the world. He'd even grown a beard!

* * * * * * * * *

The heart stopped a few times but we kept charting its steady course. Twenty months later the same Serbian team returned to Iraq. For a cool million greenbacks they picked up the last remnants of a people held in captivity for over 30 years. All the people stranded for so long in that camp now call Albania home.

The UK's Secret Intelligence Service, the Ministry of Defence and the British armed forces dutifully obey what the Foreign & Commonwealth Office in London instructs them. The popular saying at the FCO is, "Diplomacy is the art of letting other people have your way."

Yes, indeed. *Whatever works, works. But you first have to kick the ball at the goal to score.*

* * * * * * * * *

Chapter Eight

The large influx of immigrants from third world countries has significantly altered the demographic make-up of most western democracies. By now a number of western nations must have realised that a fundamental change to their national character may also be taking place. They have become more diverse societies. Often the immigrants arriving from distant lands, do so with or without the blessings of the original inhabitants. At times, the migration is caused by economic upheavals, military conflicts and refugee crises. At other times, capitalism itself with its need for cheap labour serves as a powerful magnet for new arrivals. Despite efforts to stem the flow of illegal émigrés, the human spirit will always find a way to circumvent the system.

The European countries that once ruled the colonies, have now to contend with waves of new settlers seeking to live in the mother country (or father country, depending on cultural preference). Many capitals and major cities in Western Europe have experienced the most significant change in their demographic mix. The Real McCoy of only 25 years ago has effectively disappeared and has been replaced in many neighbourhoods, by foreigners. In the blink of an eye, the initial residents have become minorities in their lifetime and in their own backyard. Many city dwellers (at least those who could afford the move), have relocated to suburbia or even to the countryside. Others simply stayed put until they deceased.

Most fair-minded people can accept the reality that non-nationals are here among us for good as long as the newcomers are willing to assimilate, pay their taxes, and obey the law. In time, they and their offspring, will gradually adopt our own nationality and become citizens through naturalisation or birth right.

You only need to look at the make-up of most national sports teams to grasp the societal changes that are slowly occurring. Nowhere is it truer than in football (known as soccer in only a handful of nations), the primary pastime in most countries. For example, the national team selection of England includes in its roster a significant number of players hailing from distant lands. Several players of Turkish or Polish ancestry play in the German squad. Similarly, the French starting 11 includes many players of African or Arab descent. It is fair to assume that this trend toward assimilation will continue.

To be sure, there's also a movement in the opposite direction. Nowadays, about 150,000 Brits live and work in France and twice that number call Spain their home. These are still small numbers, but they are not insignificant trends. When I lived in Belize (formerly British Honduras), before the turn of the century, 10,000 Mennonites (similar to the Amish) lived there among a total population of 220,000. They were more fluent in Dutch and German than in English. In Canada's biggest metropolis, Toronto, Hong Kong Chinese are the largest ethnic minority. I have met people in the United States who had lived there for more than 30 years and still cannot speak English. Sydney in Australia has a large population of Lebanese.

In any case, I have often questioned the purpose of borders. Generally, people who are sufficiently determined to leave their country of birth, can practically live wherever they want to. Many countries are finding that immigration quotas are hard to enforce. At the same time, they are struggling to prevent illegal entry.

Nowadays, many European countries are facing the prospect of a 'silent war' that is threatening to wreak havoc on them and destabilise their societies. The nations who until a short time ago had opened their doors to new immigrants, now find themselves struggling to contain the influx. It is a threat that raises its ugly head every once in a while, breaking through the surface. Sadly, many people are not sufficiently informed to appreciate the danger it presents. I liken this development to a cancer. It has already eaten away into the fabric of our society. And this problem has nothing to do with medicine.

The problems start with those few malcontents among the newcomers. They have absolutely no desire to integrate within our society. Instead, they want the citizens of their adopted country to conform to their ways of doing things. This is clearly a violation of all norms and rules of conduct. Their demands are simply unacceptable, and are wholly disrespectful towards their hosts. It becomes a major problem when they choose to kill us in our own lands, as some do. I had lived several years in the United States but, for the most part, I didn't enjoy my time there. In the end, I took a piece of sane advice from the Americans themselves, "If you don't like living here, then you should leave." So I left and moved onto greener pastures, more suited to my lifestyle and my political inclinations. *I strongly suspect, however, that these miscreants are not likely to follow my advice anytime soon.*

Because of what I did for a living, I am well aware that the security services of most free societies have their hands full monitoring the enemy now living among us. To sort out the bad boys from their law-abiding brethren is akin to finding a needle in a haystack. But with the prevalence of social media, some of the bad apples trip themselves up. A few cases come to light through the media. But in most other instances, public safety issues are never disclosed. How this situation came about is largely due to political correctness (PC). There are certain subjects that are rarely open for discussion. Most interestingly, the groups who oppose open debate of those subjects have taken full advantage of the PC climate that has taken hold. Some of the extremist elements look at this as a weakness to be fully exploited. In two decades such believers have got their roots in deep, because they have been hiding behind this perceived righteous ruling. Over the years, those that went against the grain and attempted to rock the applecart, were shouted down and were effectively silenced. In time, decency and plain-speaking have been devalued. Those readers in the know, are fully aware of what those subjects are. Reminds me of how communism ran in the old day. What you don't say, is what is meant. It has come back to haunt us and now we pay the price for this folly.

The Universal Declaration of Human Rights, which was adopted in

Paris on 10 December 1948, stating, 'All human beings are born free and equal in dignity and rights' obviously does not apply in this particular case. Even the French realised this with the passage of a law banning burqas on 13 July 2010. In Britain people cannot cover their heads with hoods in shopping centres, due to identification issues. Yet the wearing of burqas is permissible.

Over a century after women were given the right to vote in the UK, there is one main increasingly threadbare rope running through our lives that progressively keeps sliding backwards. It is only because of our continuing insistence of ignoring Muslim extremists. They are the most virulent cancer to the fabric of our society. So the more we let these anarchists get their way, the more destabilised our society becomes.

* * * * * * * * *

I fear you will never reach Mecca, O Nomad!
For the roads which you are following leads to Turkestan!
– Saadi Sharazi, Persian poet 1201-1292

Back in the late 1960's, when I was still a teenager, I took a keen interest in understanding the different religions – given that I had already developed a natural inclination and affinity towards atheism. I was still young then and I was willing to be persuaded otherwise. So, I embarked on a quest to educate myself on the various religions. I rigorously read the Holy Bible from cover to cover. Soon thereafter, I also delved into the English version of the Koran *(Quo'ran)* and studied it with the same intensity.

After completing my spiritual exploration, I could not escape the fact that both so-called sacred volumes are, to my inquisitive mind, far from being sacrosanct. They simply clash with my pacifist worldview. Most disconcertedly, they contain teachings that if taken literally, often advocate for violence and even death against those who do not share the same beliefs. To claim that either Christianity or Islam are ancient religions that promote *peace* is, in my opinion, disingenuous and somewhat of a myth. This is especially true with respect to Islam, a religion of 1.6 billion adherents mainly spread over South Asia, the Middle East and Africa.

During the last decade or two, Islam has become a focus of intense scrutiny. It has managed to radicalise a small fraction of its young adherents to commit acts of violence and terror, while professing uncompromising loyalty to their religion and their God *(Allah)*. In the name of Allah those decidedly fringe followers of Islam continue to pray in mosques. Above all, they show a willingness to even die in pursuit of violence against innocent civilians whom they consider infidels. These demented individuals somehow believe that their acts of terrorism will earn them a passport to 'martyrdom' and allow them to swiftly move on to better pastures, or as they refer to, a better afterlife. Sadly, some misguided followers of Islam choose to take the wrong path. *Apparently, for those lost souls Life starts after Death.*

Judaism, the other ancient religion, also has a chequered past of violence as evidenced by the numerous passages in the Bible seemingly promoting killings and other forms of corporal punishment. To its credit, however, Judaism has long stopped advocating for the physical elimination of its enemies. With barely 15 million adherents, Jews around the world could ill afford to antagonise their more numerous Christian and Muslim neighbours. Over the two millennia since their expulsion from the Holy Land, Jews had themselves been the target of unrelenting persecution, antisemitism and periodic pogroms. By and large, Jews had hardly the willingness or the means to pursue their enemies. Rather, they were more afraid of violence committed against them by their Christian and Muslim brethren.

And if we are talking about past excesses, let us not forget Christian atrocities committed in the name of Jesus. And, yes, Jesus Christ himself was a Jew, we all knew that. But that did not prevent Christians from killing Jews in the name of their god. Christians embarked on the deadly Crusades against the Muslim infidels (known to the latter as the wars of the cross or *al-hurab al-salabiyya)*. Christianity also implemented the infamous Spanish Inquisition. Similarly, and under the guise of Manifest Destiny, American settlers pushed westwards and were responsible for the near annihilation of the native Indians. It was just another instance of violence committed in the name of 'peace-loving' Christianity.

To their credit, the Western democracies have finally come to recognise the futility of open warfare. In the aftermath of two world wars in the 20th century and the carnage they left behind, these European nations have come to their collective senses. For the most part, they have avoided any major warfare on the European continent, if one discounts the non-state actors (terrorist groups) like the religious-instigated violence in Northern Ireland, the Basques' ETA's fight against Spain and the genocide in the Balkans by Serbian nationalists.

I could go on and comment about atrocities committed by Hindus, Sikhs, or the Greek and Russian Orthodox churches against their perceived enemies, and vice versa on them. The reader will surely realise by now that there is plenty of hatred to spread around.

Naturally, I have also perused the classic treatise first published in 1811, by Percy Bysshe Shelley. Titled *The Necessity of Atheism and Other Essays*, the publication more than validates my belief in godlessness, a tenet I have accepted from a very young age. Understandably, I wholeheartedly recommend it over the other two books.

* * * * * * * *

Desperate men are easily persuaded because
they wish desperately to be persuaded.

– JK Galbraith

When I finally retired from my career as an SIS covert action intelligence officer, some 40 years later, I diligently reread the Koran for a second time. In this instance, my exercise was much more rigorous and involved a great deal of cross-referencing. I was more than eager to learn why in the last two decades this one major religion has been the source and the cause of so much mayhem and violence. Based on raw statistics, no reasonable person could dispute the fact that the majority of random killing sprees perpetrated against innocent people, are committed by modern-day unhinged criminals who pretend to act in the name of their god, whoever and wherever he or she is. They often justify their actions as merely a response to injustices committed by 'imperialist' forces against their Muslim brethren. They resent the presence of US government and its military in Muslim countries, and the so-called war on terror that often results in the killing of innocent civilians. There is some validity to this thinking. By the

180

often-indiscriminate bombing by their air force, the Americans have managed to antagonise the masses and, some say, have become a recruitment office for the extremists in foreign lands. But over time those terrorists have reached mainland Europe and are now living among us. However, they don't refer to themselves as extremists or terrorists. They prefer to use the Arabic term of *ghûlat*, which loosely means separatists.

One has only to just examine the most recent terrorist attacks to recognise that the overwhelming majority of incidents that occurred in Western Europe can be directly linked to Muslim fanatics. They have legally emigrated to or were given safe haven as refugees. The list of violent attacks is quite extensive. The statistics do not include the 'minor' incidents which did not result in a loss of life and those other plots that were foiled before they could be carried out. Europol claim the latter outnumbers actual occurrences by a ratio of two to one.

I found the answer to what fuels this action, or rather, I re-discovered it. To my mind, the Koran clearly supports holy war *(jihad)* and spreads the notion that unbelievers *(kafirs)* are evil. I suspect that any moderate Muslim theologian *(mullah)* or cleric *(imam)* would lose a discussion with a holy warrior *(jihadi)* on who follows the instructions proscribed by the Koran more faithfully. (A mullah is one learned in theology and sacred law. An imam is one who leads the prayer in a mosque.) The vast majority of Muslims categorically state that they do not support radicalism and that such thinking is forbidden *(haram)*. In their defence, they claim that anyone who thinks otherwise, is corrupting and perverting the true nature of Islam. But to sceptical me, this argument rings hollow. How else can the defenders of Islam explain the very specific commands spread liberally across the Koran? Taken literally, the way of the Prophet *(Sunnah)* sounds to me like he is dictating how to treat infidels or persons who do not follow Islam. In my count, the so-called Islamic book on 'peace' has more than a hundred entries that I interpret as an active call to its believers to kill unbelievers. This mind-boggling number of belligerent citations corresponds to at least one instance every six pages in the 611 pages *of the copy I own*. I am not including in all this the 108 verses of teachings to wage jihad.

Is there ever a war that does not involve violence, I ask? Apologists advise us not to interpret the text literally but rather figuratively. It is a call to adherents to rally around their god in the same way that the terms 'War on Poverty' or 'War on Drugs' are often used. Some may accept this or a similar argument. But I beg to differ. Consider that the word peace *(salām)* and the other word associated with peace, like tranquillity *(sakīnah)*, appear in the Koran just a total of half a dozen times. The often-used response by Muslim supporters that people who kill in the name of Allah are not true Muslims is honestly wearing a bit thin on me, and on a sizeable majority of secular people in the UK and in Western Europe. Note: The word secular has been wilfully misinterpreted by the politically-correct but it means no connection to religion.

If you accept the basic premise of my analysis so far, would you not agree that the Koran could inspire fringe elements of Islam to become radicalised and resort to extremism, fanaticism and hatred of the western way of life?

* * * * * * * *

If Sharia law is implemented, then you can turn this country (the UK) into a haven of peace because once a thief's hand is cut off nobody is going to steal. Once, just only once, if an adulterer is stoned nobody is going to commit this crime at all. We want to offer it to the British society. If they accept it, it is for their good and if they don't accept it they'll need more and more prisons.

– Suhaib Hasan, Secretary General of the Islamic Sharia Council

To understand fully the magnitude of the challenge faced by the British domestic security services, it would be useful to compare today's problems with the conflict of a prior era. During the Troubles in Northern Ireland, the province's entire population numbered 3 million. Among them, there were 300,000 Catholic sympathisers of the militant Irish Republican Army, but only 3,000 of them were paying members. Of these, 300 were actively involved in plotting attacks, and 30 were in the actual murder squad. The conflict and the ensuing mayhem took half a century to resolve and some of the aftereffects are still lingering on.

As matters stand, *the number of Muslims residing in the UK is now almost identical to the population of Northern Island. So, you can gain some perspective on the problems we face.* The main distinction, apart from their respective callings, is the 'praying members' among the Muslim community currently living in the

UK. Mosques serve as a breeding ground for radicalism, extremism, and in time, become a recruiting tool for jihadists – leading them to becoming *mujahideen* (literal meaning: people engaged in jihad/war). In short, some of the worshippers become direct security threats that must be closely monitored. According to Interpol assessments, the threats posed by Muslim radicals, are far greater than anything the IRA offered.

Most people are not generally aware that there are over 50 different versions of the Bible. The Koran has around 20 different versions, reflecting, in some cases differences between the various sects of Islam. Despite the slight differences between the various editions, I have to believe that all essentially preach the same intolerant message. Among the various sects, Wahhabism is, by all accounts, the most violent Islamic sect (Sufism is the next most repressive faction of Islam).

To date, the Saudis have reportedly spent, since the turn of the century, upwards of £100 billion globally to advance an agenda that is hard-line, anti-west, and militaristic in equal measure. I believe that the massive infusion of cash is the feeding line to a cultural incubator that aims to radicalise as many adherents as it can and to promote hatred towards the west. British and American politicians seem to be unaware and behind the curve on the active financing of the enemy within. Instead they choose to focus on increased sales of sophisticated weaponry to Saudi Arabia as a remedy to Islamic fanaticism. In a perverse way, they are inadvertently creating a monster that ultimately will kill many innocents on both sides of the divide.

Observant Muslim men who have emigrated to western climates, tend to view the local women through the prism of their religion and their upbringing. As an example, it was once publicised that 'females have one quarter the brainpower of males'. Men like these are unforgiving of women who prefer to go around in western attire that actually accentuates their femininity. To these old-fashioned men, women are instantly deemed as worthless and treated as whores. The fact no competent chaperone/protector *(mahram)* is accompanying a female relative is a part in their thinking, too, as it risks damaging their family's dignity and reputation. Worse for Muslim women is having a guardian *(wali)* who is responsible for finding her the most suitable spouse to marry. For men, sex, even the non-consensual version, is a God-given right. If females don't cover themselves then they actually invite unwanted sexual advances and even rape. In short, they deserve what's coming to them. Remarkably, that attitude prevails on underage girls as well. Such lines of reasoning are deplorable. Assault and rape has no part in any society. No 'ifs', 'ands' or 'buts'. When arrested for sex crime, to blame religion for one's actions is a cop out from moral responsibility.

Another aspect of Islam that often is an irritant to westerners, and the object of much frustration, is the custom of wearing a face veil *(hijab)* and full body gown *(burqa)*. The practice for Muslim women starts at puberty. The dress code is enforced by pressure from family, peer groups or social circles. It is explained as a way to ensure modesty according to the teachings of the Koran. By its very nature, however, the code is another discriminatory practice imposed by men against females to ensure male domination of the fairer sex. This draconian diktat has been in play since medieval times. This is now the 21st century. (Interestingly the times that pre-date Islam are called 'the time of ignorance'.)

Those that choose to ignore the code, are often threatened with punishment by a court of a council of men *(sharia)*. Open-minded and liberal Muslims living in the freedom of the west, find the requirement for a woman to wear a veil or full body gown, a sign of disrespect to western values and the rule of secular law. The shroud covering the face is a clear act of repression of women's rights normally enjoyed in western lands. *Some non-Muslim apologists in the west mistakenly think women have a free choice on this matter. The sad reality is that for strictly observant Muslims, more often than not, women cannot exercise their choice without severe repercussions from the males who incessantly hover over them. Men are the ones who are deciding for them.*

Another issue of deep concern to me, pertains to implementation of the law in the UK as it applies to Muslims. It is unofficially believed that there are up to 20,000 polygamous marriages within the Muslim community of Britain. According to sharia law, men are permitted to marry up to four wives, in clear violation of British civil law. If this flaunting of civil law is permitted to take hold, then in due time, sharia law can become a parallel legal system that will clash with the existing legal system on bigamy.

The framers of western governance systems have wisely recognised that there is a need for strict separation between 'church and state'. The government will not interfere with the practice of religion as long as those religious groups do not engage in activities that clash with civilian law. For example, Jews, Muslims or any other religious sect can pass their own dietary rules forbidding the consumption of specific foods such as pork. Likewise, they can designate *kosher* food or *halal* meats. This is an edict that means that foodstuffs must be prepared in accordance to strict religious instructions. In all instances, however, these rules must conform to the wider regulations issued by the civilian authorities. The same criteria apply to marriage, circumcision and other pious rites.

I have no problem at all with such laws. What I object to, is the emergence of a parallel legal system that can ignore civilian law and possibly operate as an independent and parallel legal system.

In Britain, there are several examples of cities where Muslims represent a majority in some neighbourhoods. In those instances, sharia police are reportedly operating in no-go zones where nonbelievers are banned, or at least discouraged from entering them. This is especially true on streets where a mosque is located. Anybody who walks down that road must be dressed in accordance with Islamic law. They cannot display flesh on their arms and legs for example. Such a person is not permitted to carry alcohol either.

Where I live in France, Muslims comprise fully 7.5% of the total population. The legal and moral challenges facing French authorities are already well recognised. Attempts are under way to address the thorny problem: ensuring the rule of law to all without infringing on the freedom of Muslims and other groups to practice their religion. Within the UK, movement towards resolving this conundrum has taken slow and tentative steps at best. The overriding fear is to be politically-correct (PC). In the UK, for example, one only has to utter a word of criticism of a minority to be immediately accused of racism, whether the allegation is true or false. So, the truth is immediately side-tracked, never to be explored. PC is a method of fighting an incorrectness with another incorrectness, a bit like eating oneself. This movement is also coupled with the British government's dread of offending Saudi Arabia's sensibilities, whose religious components openly fund Islamic zealotry globally, along with its equally fervent counterparts in Qatar and Iran.

I am only an intermediary but I am forced to figuratively wear a bullet-proof vest to deliver the message, which already tells anybody that freedom of speech is curtailed in Britain when it comes to this particular subject matter. *The armour around it is the cleverly constructed fence of being PC which serves up the whitewashed version.* And for the record my politics are mainly left of centre. But the liberal agenda pushed on us has moved too far away from common sense.

The whole idea of living our life is to live without fear.

The content you have just read is not a tin-foil theory but an informed opinion based on many years of personal research of the issue, coupled with life experience. We must stand up to Islamic extremists who want to subvert our secular and legal system and supplant it with a medieval and a deeply flawed one. We have the right to resist the fanatic fringe of Islam from oppressing us in our own mostly secular (non-religious) country.

We must also understand that there is virtually no critical thinking in Islam. The reason is because *Allah knows and decides everything on followers' behalf, who are not responsible for their actions.* So we must put answers and accountability in place for them. After a crime, for the police to seek what an Islamist's motivation is, dictates ignorance of the issue, when the answer is hidden in plain sight.

An important step towards the assimilation of Muslims in our society is to free Muslim women from the bonds that currently shackle many of them. The second step is to clarify our intent and enforce British judicial law to ensure full freedom for Muslim women, much like France has done. To stand by and do nothing at all will only aggravate the plight of Muslim women. Time is not on our side.

There is a simple test that can be put in place to prevent undesirable elements from entering our country. In this regard we can implement a light version of the UK citizenship test for newly arrived refugees seeking a safe haven from destitution, persecution or conflict. Under the new system these refugees would have to:

1. Pledge allegiance to honour our way of life
2. Make bona fide efforts to assimilate into our society

After registering for asylum, they would, in the presence of translators, have to sign a document (also available in their mother language). The document will be far from a written oath of unconditional loyalty *(bayyah)*. It will however weed out those who will not accept our laws. If you want to stay in this country, you must agree to peacefully observe our liberties. Quite possibly, a small percentage will absolutely refuse on the spot to sign such a declaration. Others will hesitate. Their true sentiment will be etched on their faces. It is a visual and early warning signal of their disagreement with the non-legally binding form. It will separate those seeking true freedom from those who view our country merely as a land of disbelief *(duh-al-kufah)* or the material world *(dunyah)*. Admittedly, the proposed filtering tool is not full-proof. It can be circumvented, but the pledge requirement in writing is likely to weed out the malcontents from the legitimate refugees. It will be done at an early time and before they are able to enjoy the largesse we afford them or to create mischief in our midst.

It's the perfect storm of a bad situation. We must be proactive about immigration into our lands. We must do all we can to prevent those who are not like-minded about our society and values, nor want to be, from reaching our shores. Otherwise, what is the point of state borders at all? We might as well dismantle them altogether and allow the free entry to our country to anybody, and allow them to go anywhere they please. Perhaps, even the centuries-old names of nations as we currently know them on the global map may have to be changed. Timidity in the enforcement of secular laws, excessive fear of trampling on human rights and ear-bashing political correctness, may in due time render such given monikers entirely irrelevant in this modern day and age. Formerly known as the United Kingdom of Great Britain and Northern Ireland, a rather long name to have, may take the name of Al-Brittani (translates in Arabic to British) as the replacement. With its new name, this once proud country may well slide from the fifth richest economy in the world to an also-ran country, struggling to deal with it downgraded status among nations. Simultaneously, in no time at all the UK has gone from being secular to sectarian (religious).

According to a 2017 estimate, Muslims represented 5% of the population in the UK. If we leave things the way they are, then by the year 2047, a British Caucasian like me, will live in a country where fully 10% of its inhabitants will be Muslim. This demographic projection is predicated on the premise that for British Caucasians the net growth rate (birth minus death) is 0.5% per year, while for Muslims the net growth (birth minus death) is 1.5%.

By comparison, in countries such as France, Belgium, Germany, Switzerland and the Netherlands, Muslims represent 6.0% to 7.5% of the total population. *The estimates are based on the latest statistics reported by the national census.* According to this data, Islam is now the second largest religion in Western Europe after Christianity.

I am already in the less than 40% when I visit London. It is the challenge of our generation to prevent further erosion of who we are. Otherwise, within the next 30 years we may experience continuing acts of terrorism and the random bombing of innocents on a regular basis...

To avoid this dire scenario, we must wake up one day, and do it soon before it's too late to change tack. *This is the belly of the beast* (batn al-gul) *we are faced with. As I see it, this is the Arab way of exacting revenge for the betrayal of them committed by our forefathers after World War I. At the time, Britain and France concocted the imperialist Sykes-Picot Agreement that controversially divided up territories in the Middle East between the two superpowers. Despite the perceived injustices from years past,* it is important to call these people that want to kill us and destroy our way of life, for what they are: racists, fascists, supremacists and incorrigible haters. Otherwise, why would they keep bombing us and in the process kill and maim innocent civilians on a regular basis? Please ask yourself that question before we surrender completely and submit our soul to Allah *(zikr)* and its twisted ideology.

Islamic State's news agency, *Amaq* (Versatile), and its newspaper, *Al-Naba* (The News), will report otherwise though!

To close: the saying 'the early bird gets the worm' comes to mind about this situation, but its antonym is 'life punishes those who come late'.

If liberty means anything at all,
it means the right to tell people what they do not want to hear.

– George Orwell

PS: When Britain voted (to) Leave the European Union, resulting in Brexit, its most well-known critic, a Remain campaign pollster named Andrew Cooper famously summed the result up with, "We struggled to communicate a complex truth in the face of simple lies." I have done my best to constructively criticise and point out danger areas. If we fail to act decisively against virulent Muslim extremism in our own lands, I do not want to be using a similar quote in the years to come. But, at the time of writing, we are casually watching a car crash coming right at us. Not only does the law have to be urgently changed but our cultural attitude needs shaking up.

* * * * * * * * *

Epilogue

The discovery that male chimpanzees mount organised attacks on other chimpanzee groups raises the uncomfortable possibility that there is a genetic element involved – that, in short, human beings are programmed for socially organised violence.

— AC Grayling, author, *War: An Enquiry*

George Young, was a British intelligence officer who until his retirement in 1961, held senior level positions in the SIS. After his departure, he became a case study and a *cause celebre* in my training class. I'm not sure whether it was about following his example or not following his example. Nevertheless, in the mid-fifties he warned of disturbing political trends beginning to take shape at that time. He argued that in the press, in Parliament, in the United Nations and from the pulpit, there was an unrelenting barrage of self-serving pontification masquerading as serious discourse. He firmly believed in the rule of law and the necessity for civilised relations between nations. At other times, he argued passionately for the spread of democratic ideals to the less-enlightened countries, self-determination and national sovereignty, respect for human rights and protection of individual's dignity.

Unfortunately, people like me who followed in his footsteps a decade later, had to confront a vastly different reality from the ideals he preached. As I see it, an ever-increasingly level of political gridlock, lawlessness, cruelty and corruption are taking hold. It's a culture of concealment, no less, and it is becoming more acceptable as time goes by. Governments themselves have created this miasma and, in effect, have morphed into organisations no longer able or fit to govern. To my mind, voting for political parties is an obsolete concept. We should be polling instead on specific policy options. Secure and encrypted technology is already available to implement these changes within our societies.

The cold war, for me, was never a conflict between capitalism and communism. Rather, it was a struggle for liberation of the people on *both* sides of the curtain and the wall. And now that the barriers have been torn down, we're still fighting against the systematic distortion of the truth. But the frontlines have shifted. *In this day and age, the real enemy is unregulated capitalism. It is shamelessly supported by an unbalanced and complicit media, willingly doing its part to bend the minds and hearts of the gullible masses.* To counter this crunching gear change towards oblivion of democratic ideals, more power should be vested in setting mechanisms that promote competition and free markets. Such bodies should have the authority to audit and expose corrupt or monopolistic practices. The alarming shift was caused, in part, by the emergence of information technology as a powerful tool for capitalism to exert economic leverage over the less developed nations. If anything, the new expertise has now replaced oil and gas production as a means for commercial control and domination. Computers and robotics working silently on algorithms attract less attention than big, noisy installations and refineries.

To achieve and perpetuate control of the levers of power, conspiracy theories often originate inside the government itself. In many cases, the schemes are instigated to throw the public off the real scent. The ruling élite can point to neat coincidences and maintain a proper façade of plausible 'deniability'. It is all a strategy to create tension, to distract from huge profits generated by the ruling class. And when 'conspiracy theories' are found to have a strong semblance to the truth, the government, through its mates in the compliant media, can dismiss the story as 'in the realms of the fantastic'. Stern officials can then step up to the microphone and duly deny the 'inconvenient truth'. Sadly, even when real Truth emerges, it is often hard to discern from the fake news. Facts become sacred but it is a term nobody can quite define. It becomes difficult to differentiate facts from 'alternate facts'. *This is all purposefully designed by the establishment. It has the governments in its pocket, who in turn are tasked with keeping the rank and file tax payers at bay.*

The same old song and dance routine practiced by politicians has been going on for decades. The lip service and continuing impunity needs to be stopped. We now have a lot of escapologists within the upper echelons of our governments. They throw us daily scraps of hypocrisy and hyperbole, all rolled into one to feast on. I once thought that the original objective of the news outlets was to hold those in power to account. Unfortunately, they've succumbed to the collective dumbing down of the people and are now a big part of the problem. At SIS, before my time, deliberate fibs were euphemistically expressed as 'unattributable propaganda'. During my career these same outright lies became known as pieces of 'disinformation'. Nowadays 'fake news' has become the term used to describe lies. Irrespective of what you call them, these fancy permutations describe intentional distortions in the mass media aimed at confusing us and adversely affecting our ability to judge. In this regard, when presented with real and fake news, you must ask yourself, 'Who stands to benefit from this?' This may give you a clue as to the correct answer.

The gutter press – red tops in the UK – are especially guilty. As a result, we the people gradually lose our capacity to think for ourselves. In short, we become entrenched in our positions and rely on the fourth estate and those in power to carefully feed us the self-serving selection of 'alternate facts' they want us to believe in. But if you are able to open your eyes, what you are actually witnessing is loads of pretention, shams, reframing of the sequence of events, and so forth. The history of the world is replete with tragic outcomes that could have been prevented with a little more foresight. Unfortunately, those with eyes simply refused to see, and those with ears failed to hear. The dumbing down with nonstop escapism is almost complete – with this avoidance of realism.

The list of major failures is long. Prominent examples of absolute meltdowns include the rise of Nazism, the Vietnam War, the illegal invasion of Iraq, the rise of Muslim extremism, among others.

Just to remind the reader of the dangers of complacency which our society faces, consider the apathy that eventually led to the rise of Adolf Hitler. The unchecked madness of Nazism eventually triggered the cataclysmic World War II, with its millions of casualties and refugees. At first only Jews were targeted for brutal oppression and disenfranchisement. Then came the genocide of the mentally disabled, the gypsies, the clergy, the intellectual class and finally the entire German population. Hitler was underestimated because it was difficult for people to conceive that he was hell-bent on world domination…

This poem perhaps best sums up this situation and, hopefully, will not be repeated again:

> *First they came for the Socialists, and I did not speak out –*
> *because I was not a Socialist.*
> *Then they came for the Trade Unionists, and I did not speak out –*
> *because I was not a Trade Unionist.*
> *Then they came for the Jews, and I did not speak out –*
> *because I was not a Jew.*
> *Then they came for me – and there was no one left to speak for me.*

The man who wrote this, Martin Niemöller (1892–1984), was a prominent German Protestant pastor who was an outspoken public foe of Adolf Hitler and spent the last seven years of Nazi rule in concentration camps.

More recently the world is still smarting from a more recent catastrophic war in Iraq. It was cooked up by neocons, and launched by a naïve George W. Bush, with the aid of our own Tony Blair. Again, the lies are too extraordinarily long to list here but many of the current generation know what they are.

Even as we speak there are new dangers raising their ugly heads and lurking on the horizon, as already featured in the previous chapter…

During my career in SIS, too many officials refused to comment 'in the national interest'. We must be resolute and must be willing to fight against the numbing effect of conventional wisdom. Turning to those who say they can fix the problems is not the answer, *because the current political system is already obsolete*, long dead and buried. *It's a different beast now.* The answer is to do it yourself. It starts with changing the system you have grown comfortable with, and stepping out into an uncomfortable zone. The local community is a good place to start advancing ideas. From there the concepts can organically and gradually spread. In other words: take control of your own destiny.

My personal remit, in writing my account, was to tell those who won't listen to all the things they don't want to know. I hope I changed the perceptions of some readers, and perhaps, the predestined course of our world can be altered for the better.

Mine is a life *lived*. I can say that I certainly walked with destiny. And I've thought there must have been a reason for that. So In telling my story it is…closure.

So how can one find out what's Truth and what isn't? I think Antoine de Saint-Expéry got it right when he wrote, *'It is only with the heart that one can see clearly. What's essential is invisible to the eye.'* If you feel an instinct then that's the best way to determine what is and what isn't. Essentially, experience of life educates the heart. The absence of life experience doesn't educate the heart.

Another piece of advice I've heeded is by François-Marie Arouet, otherwise known as Voltaire, who said, *'To learn who rules over you, simply find out who you are not allowed to criticise.'* Indeed, that is so true, as I have learned to my cost.

I'll end this fourth book of mine by borrowing the appropriate words from an excellent advertisement by the British bookshop organisation, *National Book Tokens*. *NBT* is focused mainly on encouraging youth to read more, but should promote more adults to do the same…with more intelligent material:

Somewhere beneath A Thousand Splendid Suns
you drift towards a Brave New World.
The Sea stretches out before you
as you pass Fantastic Beasts and Beautiful Creatures.
For Days Without End you consider
How to Stop Worrying and Start Living
when suddenly you spy Treasure Island.
You reach The Beach and head off Into the Wild.
This Must be the Place, you think.
And sure enough, beyond
The River Cottage, and just East of Eden,
you find what you're looking for.

<THE END>

Lightning Source UK Ltd.
Milton Keynes UK
UKHW021152100220
358475UK00013B/3483